GOTHAM
CENTRAL

POLICE

ALIS

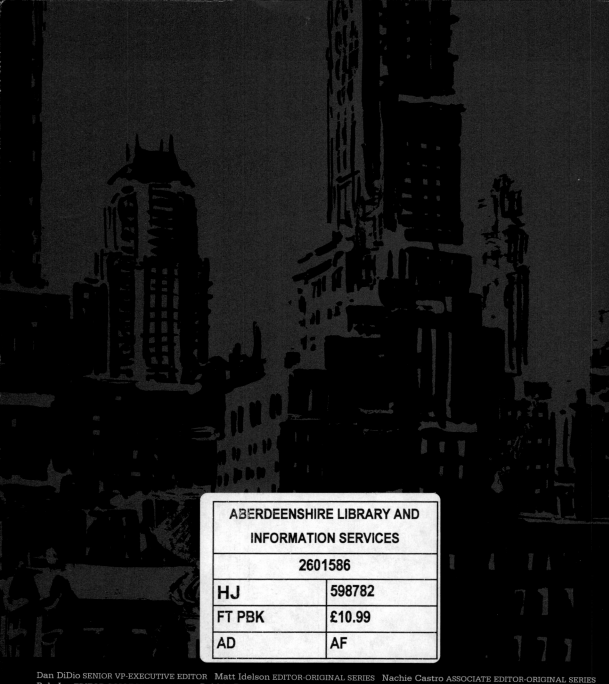

Dan DiDio SENIOR VP-EXECUTIVE EDITOR   Matt Idelson EDITOR-ORIGINAL SERIES   Nachie Castro ASSOCIATE EDITOR-ORIGINAL SERIES
Bob Joy EDITOR-COLLECTED EDITION   Robbin Brosterman SENIOR ART DIRECTOR   Paul Levitz PRESIDENT & PUBLISHER
Georg Brewer VP-DESIGN & DC DIRECT CREATIVE   Richard Bruning SENIOR VP-CREATIVE DIRECTOR
Patrick Caldon EXECUTIVE VP-FINANCE & OPERATIONS   Chris Caramalis VP-FINANCE   John Cunningham VP-MARKETING
Terri Cunningham VP-MANAGING EDITOR   Alison Gill VP-MANUFACTURING   Hank Kanalz VP-GENERAL MANAGER, WILDSTORM
Jim Lee EDITORIAL DIRECTOR-WILDSTORM   Paula Lowitt SENIOR VP-BUSINESS & LEGAL AFFAIRS
MaryEllen McLaughlin VP-ADVERTISING & CUSTOM PUBLISHING   John Nee VP-BUSINESS DEVELOPMENT
Gregory Noveck SENIOR VP-CREATIVE AFFAIRS   Sue Pohja VP-BOOK TRADE SALES   Cheryl Rubin SENIOR VP-BRAND MANAGEMENT
Jeff Trojan VP-BUSINESS DEVELOPMENT, DC DIRECT   Bob Wayne VP-SALES

Cover art by Sean Phillips
Publication design by Amie Brockway-Metcalf

GOTHAM CENTRAL™

DEAD ROBIN

GREG RUCKA WRITER

KANO PENCILLER

STEFANO GAUDIANO INKER

CLEM ROBINS LETTERER

LEE LOUGHRIDGE COLORIST

"DEAD ROBIN" CHAPTERS CO-WRITTEN BY
ED BRUBAKER

"SUNDAY BLOODY SUNDAY" CHAPTER ART BY
STEVE LIEBER

BATMAN CREATED BY **BOB KANE**

**CAPTAIN
MAGGIE SAWYER**
First shift commander;
formerly head of Metropolis
Special Crimes Unit.

**SGT. VINCENT
DEL ARRAZIO**
First shift commander;
First shift second-in-command;
partner of Joely Bartlett.

**DETECTIVE
TOMMY BURKE**
Partner of
Dagmar Procjnow.

**DETECTIVE
ERIC COHEN**
Partner of Andi Kasinsky.

**DETECTIVE
ANDI KASINSKY**
Partner of Eric Cohen.

**DETECTIVE
JOSEPHINE "JOSIE
MAC" MacDONALD**
Has the distinction of being
the first MCU officer selected
after Jim Gordon's retirement.

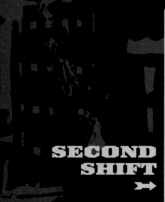

LT. DAVID CORNWELL
Second shift commander.

**SGT. JACKSON
"SARGE" DAVIES**
Second shift co-second-in-
command; partner of Crowe.

LT. RON PROBSON
Second shift co-second-in-
command.

**DETECTIVE
TREY HARTLEY**
Partner of Josh Azeveda.

**DETECTIVE
NATE PATTON**
Partner of Romy Chandler.

**COMMISSIONER
MICHAEL AKINS**
Former commissioner for
Gateway City, replaced
James W. Gordon.

**DETECTIVE
CRISPUS ALLEN**
Partner of Renee Montoya.

**DETECTIVE
JOELY BARTLETT**
Partner of Vincent
Del Arrazio.

GOTHAM CITY POLICE DEPARTMENT,

MAJOR CRIMES UNIT

**DETECTIVE 2ND GRADE
RENEE MONTOYA**
Partner of Crispus Allen.

**DETECTIVE
DAGMAR PROCJNOW**
Partner of Tommy Burke.

**DETECTIVE
JOSH AZEVEDA**
Partner of Trey Hartley.

**DETECTIVE
ROMY CHANDLER**
Partner of Nate Patton.

DETECTIVE CROWE
Partner of Sarge Davies.

**DETECTIVE
MARCUS DRIVER**
Last MCU officer to be select-
ed by former Commissioner
James W. Gordon.

JIM CORRIGAN
GCPD crime scene
investigator.

NORA FIELDS
City coroner.

JAMES W. GORDON
Former Gotham City police
commissioner, and 20-year
veteran of the force. Currently
teaches criminology at
Gotham University.

STACY
Receptionist; only person
permitted to operate the
Bat-signal.

DEAD ROBIN

In an effort to regain control over Gotham following a brutal gang war, Commissioner Akins outlawed masked vigilantes from roaming the city's streets. Officers are ordered to stop Batman and his crew by any means necessary. The Caped Crusader, not wanting to share his risk of retribution, ordered all of his colleagues to leave Gotham. Robin, along with Batgirl, was banished to Blüdhaven, where he patrols the alleys looking for crime...or does he?

IT'S **NOT** HIM.

AND YOU KNOW THAT **HOW** EXACTLY, DETECTIVE MACDONALD? ARE YOU A MEMBER OF THE TEEN TITANS ON THE SIDE, NOW?

NO, IT JUST--IT **CAN'T** BE HIM.

SHE'S **RIGHT**, CAPTAIN. IT'S TOO SIMPLE. NO SIGN OF ANYTHING OTHER THAN **IMPACT** INJURIES ON THE BODY, NOT A FACIAL CONTUSION TO SPEAK OF.

WHICH SAYS TO ME HE FELL...YET HE'S GOT HIS **GRAPPLE** THING RIGHT HERE. DOESN'T MAKE SENSE.

HE COULD'VE ENDED UP LYING HERE **ANY** NUMBER OF WAYS, DETECTIVE DRIVER.

THESE PEOPLE **DO** FIGHT ON THOSE ROOFTOPS, **REMEMBER**? HE COULD'VE BEEN **UNCONSCIOUS** WHEN HE WENT OVER THE SIDE.

TRUE...BUT IT STILL FEELS WRONG. THIS **ISN'T** HOW ONE OF **THEM** DIES.

AW, **GOD**... CAN'T BE **SIXTEEN**, EVEN.

YOU REALIZE, IF THIS *IS* ACTUALLY HIM, THEN EVEN IF THIS IS ACCIDENTAL, THE BAT IS AT FAULT?

ENDANGERING THE LIFE OF A MINOR... UNLESS THE *PARENTS* ARE IN ON IT, TOO, THEN THEY'RE ALL TO BLAME.

MAYBE BATMAN *IS* ONE OF THE PARENTS?

THERE'S A SCARY THOUGHT.

CAPTAIN SAWYER. DETECTIVES...

COMMISSIONER AKINS.

YOU *DO* REALIZE THERE'S *ALREADY* A MEDIA CIRCUS ACROSS THE STREET?

YEAH, THE UNIFORM MENTIONED THE CAPE ANGLE WHEN HE CALLED IT IN AND POLICE SCANNERS LIT UP ALL OVER TOWN, APPARENTLY.

WONDERFUL.

SO, WHAT ARE WE LOOKING AT? IS IT *ACTUALLY* HIM?

WE DON'T *THINK* SO, SIR... BUT WE CAN'T BE *SURE* AT THIS POINT. THE *GEAR* LOOKS PROFESSIONAL, AT LEAST.

CAUSE OF DEATH?

LOOKING LIKE A SUDDEN CASE OF *CEMENT POISONING*, SIR. SKULL CRACKED OPEN WHEN HE HIT THE PAVEMENT.

WE'LL HAVE TO WAIT FOR THE AUTOPSY FOR ANYTHING ELSE.

SO, THERE'S *NOTHING* TO FEED THE VULTURES WITH, THEN?

SORRY, SIR, NOT UNLESS MONTOYA AND ALLEN FOUND A *BLOODY UMBRELLA* OR A SIGNED *CONFESSION* ON THE ROOF...

9

BOREN, GONNA NEED SOME *SHOTS* OVER HERE.

GOT YOU COVERED, DETECTIVE.

THIS GOES *STRAIGHT* TO THE *LAB,* AND THEY PROCESS IT *IMMEDIATELY.*

YES, MA'AM.

AND MAKE SURE YOU KEEP IT AWAY FROM *CORRIGAN...*

...I DON'T WANT IT GOING *MISSING* OUT OF *EVIDENCE.*

NO, MA'AM.

BOREN, WHEN YOU'RE *DONE* HERE, WE'RE GONNA NEED SOME *SHOTS* OF THE *LEDGE.*

HOW FAR YOU FIGURE TO THE *ADJACENT* ROOFTOP, RENEE?

MAYBE *TEN* FEET ACROSS? HALF AGAIN THAT *HIGH?*

YEAH, THAT'S HOW IT *LOOKS* TO ME, TOO.

THAT SEEM *ANY* HARDER THAN THE KIND OF JUMP ROBIN WOULD *NORMALLY* MAKE?

IF YOU'RE THINKING THIS WAS AN *ACCIDENTAL* DEATH, CRIS, I'M NOT SEEING THE *EVIDENCE* ONE WAY OR THE *OTHER.*

OTHER THAN THAT *BATARANG,* I'M NOT SEEING ANY SIGN OF A *STRUGGLE,* EITHER.

SO HE GOT *DUMPED.* OR PUSHED.

HELL, *MAYBE* IT'S *SUICIDE.*

THE KID WORKED FOR *BATMAN* AFTER ALL.

GREAT. *YOU* WANT TO ASK HIM IF ROBIN'S BEEN FEELING *DEPRESSED* RECENTLY?

"HOW'S HE BEEN SLEEPING? ANY SIGNS OF *DRUG USE?* TROUBLE AT *SCHOOL?*"

WE'RE GOING TO HAVE TO TALK TO BATMAN, ONE WAY OR *ANOTHER.*

YOU DON'T *SERIOUSLY* THINK HE'S A *SUSPECT.*

HE'S THE *PRIME* SUSPECT, FAR AS I'M CONCERNED--

THAT'S *CRAP.*

--HE KNEW THE *VICTIM,* KNEW HIM *WELL.* THEY WORKED *TOGETHER.*

FORGET THAT IT'S *MAYBE* ROBIN THE BOY WONDER IN THE ALLEY AND *YOU* TELL ME HOW WE SHOULD PURSUE THIS.

ANY OTHER CASE, WE'D PUT THE *PARTNER* AT THE TOP OF THE LIST OF *SUSPECTS.*

ASSUMING THIS IS MURDER, AND WE DON'T *KNOW* THAT YET.

YEAH, *ASSUMING* IT'S--

OH MY GOD. OH MY GOD, CRIS.

THINK ABOUT IT.

IF THAT *REALLY* IS *ROBIN* AND WE *I.D.* THE BODY, EVERY-ONE'S GONNA *KNOW* WHO HE *WAS.*

OBVIOUSLY.

NO, YOU DON'T *GET* IT. WE PUT ROBIN'S *SECRET IDENTITY* UNDER THE *MICRO-SCOPE...*

...WE COULD END UP DISCOVERING *BATMAN'S,* AS WELL.

WE DONE UP HERE?

...YEAH...

...LET'S SEE WHAT JO AND MARCUS GOT, TAKE IT FROM THERE...

ROBIN'S IN *BLÜDHAVEN.*

JESUS--

THEN *WHO--*

I DON'T *KNOW.*

BUT *I'M* GOING TO FIND OUT.

STAY OUT OF MY WAY.

WAIT JUST A *SECOND,* YOU'VE GOT TO *ANSWER--*

BATMAN, *WAIT!*

STAY OUT OF MY WAY.

--IF IT REALLY IS ROBIN, COMMISSIONER?

--CONFIRM THAT THE JOKER IS STILL IN ARKHAM?

--ANY [WIT]NESSES COME [F]ORWARD?

IF YOU'LL LET ME GET A *WORD* IN, I'LL MAKE A STATEMENT.

THANK YOU.

A BODY WAS FOUND A LITTLE OVER AN HOUR AGO IN THE ALLEY BEHIND US. AS MOST OF YOU ALREADY *KNOW*, THAT BODY WAS IN A *ROBIN* COSTUME.

AT THIS EARLY STAGE OF OUR INVESTIGATION, THAT IS THE *ONLY* INFORMATION WE CAN SHARE WITH THE PRESS.

SO, YOU'RE JUST TELLING US WHAT WAS *ALREADY* LEAKED OVER THE *SCANNERS*, THEN, COMMISSIONER?

I COULD ALWAYS *DENY* IT, IF YOU'D PREFER, MR. LIPPMAN. BUT I *TRY* TO TELL THE TRUTH AS OFTEN AS POSSIBLE.

COMMISSIONER! WHAT ABOUT--

DOES THE G.C.P.D. *BELIEVE* THIS BOY IS THE *REAL* ROBIN, COMMISSIONER? OUR VIEWERS DESERVE *THAT* MUCH, AT LEAST.

AT THIS POINT, WE CAN'T *CONFIRM* HIS IDENTITY ONE WAY OR THE *OTHER*. BUT WE'RE--

WRRRROOOMM

WRRRROOOOMM

--GETTING THIS?

--YOU SHOOTING, RON? GET THIS! GET THIS!!

SSKRREEEE

WELL, THAT'S JUST *PERFECT*, ISN'T IT?

HE *REALLY* DOESN'T LIKE YOU.

COMMISSIONER! ARE YOU TELLING--

COMMISSIONER! HOW DO YOU--

ARE YOU AWARE THAT THE ...KER HAS SWORN...

THE RUMORS OF BREAKOUT AT ARKHAM?

COMMISSIONER! WHAT ABOUT--

...AS ...L OF ...AN'S ...ES?

COMMISSIONER!

YOU TAKING OFF, SIMON?

OH, *HEY*, DUNNING...YEAH, WE'RE NOT GETTING ANYTHING HERE. MIGHT AS WELL FILE BEFORE THE TV PEOPLE GET TO WORK.

THINK IT'S REALLY *HIM*? ROBIN?

SEEMS A LITTLE OFF TO ME, BUT IN *THIS* TOWN? WHO CAN SAY?

PRESS

HELL, FOR ALL WE KNOW, BATMAN'S GOT A WHOLE *FLOCK* OF ROBINS. THIS MIGHT'VE BEEN A *TRAINEE* OR SOMETHING.

HUNH, YEAH, *GOOD POINT.* WHAT A WORLD, HUHN?

YOU SAID.

DRIVER "ROBIN"

ALL RIGHT, SETTLE DOWN...

...LET'S DO THIS BY THE NUMBERS.

AT SEVENTEEN PAST MIDNIGHT THIS MORNING, DOCTOR RAYMOND ALEXANDER OF 4422 SOUTH HENDERSON DISCOVERED THE BODY OF A YOUNG MAN DEAD IN THE ALLEY BEHIND HIS APARTMENT BUILDING.

AN EXAMINATION OF THE COSTUME AND GEAR TAKEN FROM THE BODY ARE CONSISTENT WITH REPORTS OF ROBIN'S EQUIPMENT.

FOR THE TIME BEING, THEREFORE, WE MUST ASSUME THAT WE'RE INVESTIGATING THE DEATH OF THE BOY WONDER, AT LEAST UNTIL WE CAN PROVE OTHERWISE.

DRIVER AND MACDONALD ARE PRIMARY, ALLEN AND MONTOYA ARE SECONDARY.

MARCUS?

THE BODY'S AT THE MORGUE, JOSIE AND I ARE HEADING THERE AFTER THIS BRIEFING.

UNIFORMS FOUND A NEIGHBOR WHO SAYS THEY SAW FLASHING LIGHTS ON THE ROOFTOP EARLIER THAT NIGHT.

APPARENTLY, NOBODY SAW THE FALL...

...AT LEAST, NO ONE WHO WILL ADMIT TO IT.

A BATARANG WAS RECOVERED AT THE SCENE, IT'S AT THE LAB NOW.

OTHERWISE, NO SIGNS OF A STRUGGLE.

I WANT A **SECOND** CANVASS OF THE AREA, SEE IF WE CAN'T FIND A **WITNESS** WHO'S **WORTH** A DAMN.

SARGE, I'D LIKE YOU TO **HEAD** THAT UP, IF YOU PLEASE.

JOY.

WE LOOKING AT BATMAN FOR THIS?

HE'S THE **PRIME** SUSPECT, **RIGHT**?

WE HAD A **RUN-IN** WITH HIM ON THE **ROOF.** HE SAYS ROBIN'S IN BLÜDHAVEN.

HE **ALSO** SAYS HE'S LOOKING **INTO** IT AND THAT HE WANTS **US** TO STAY **OUT** OF IT.

DOESN'T ANSWER MY **QUESTION.**

I'D LIKE HIM TO TALK TO US.

BUT WE'RE **NOT** CALLING HIM A **SUSPECT** YET, NOT UNTIL WE HAVE SOME **EVIDENCE** THAT POINTS TO IT.

WE HAVE A **DAMN** BATARANG, CAP!

HE'S **NOT** A **SUSPECT,** DETECTIVE CHANDLER.

UNDERSTOOD?

YEAH.

ALLEN AND MONTOYA ARE HEADING OUT TO **ARKHAM** TO QUESTION THE USUAL SUSPECTS. BURKE AND PROCJNOW, YOU GO **WITH** THEM.

AS FOR THE **REST** OF YOU, START **BEATING** THE **BUSHES**, LOOK AT ALL OF ROBIN'S **KNOWN** ENEMIES AND ACQUAINTANCES.

THE **MEDIA'S** ALREADY ALL OVER THIS, KIDS.

WE'RE GONNA NEED TO MOVE **FAST**.

GET TO **WORK**.

YOU OKAY, PARTNER?

C'MON, LET'S GO **BREAK** SOME **ICE**.

...BUT YOU DIDN'T HAVE TO OVERSEE EVERYTHING PERSONALLY. YOU COULD STILL BE SLEEPING.

I LOVE THAT YOU JUST *ASSUME* I'M IN *BED* AT TWO A.M., MARCUS...

I WAS *ACTUALLY* ON A *DATE.*

--APPRECIATE YOU GETTING THIS PUSHED THROUGH ON THE *NIGHT SHIFT* FOR US, NORA...

KANE COUNTY MORGUE

YOU--YOU--Y...

YOU SHOULD *REALLY* GET THAT STUTTER LOOKED AT.

SO...WHAT'S THE *PROGNOSIS,* BILL?

LOOKING PRETTY STRAIGHTFORWARD, SO FAR.

TRAUMA IS CONSISTENT WITH A FALL FROM THE HEIGHT LISTED ON THE POLICE REPORT, ESPECIALLY THIS SKULL FRACTURE.

STILL WAITING ON THE TOX SCREEN, BUT IF HE WAS *ON* ANYTHING, HE TOOK IT *INTERNALLY.*

THERE'S NO NEEDLE MARKS ANY-WHERE ON THE BODY.

IS THERE *ANYTHING* TO TELL US WHETHER THIS IS THE REAL ROBIN OR A FAKE?

HARD TO SAY, DETECTIVE. HE FITS THE *TYPE,* DEFINITELY...

APPEARS IN GOOD SHAPE, PHYSICALLY, AND IS SOMEWHERE AROUND FIFTEEN YEARS OF AGE.

LOOKING AT HIS X-RAYS, YOU CAN SEE HE'S GOT OLD *FRACTURES* IN BOTH ARMS, AND ONE LEG.

WHICH, IF THERE *IS* A REAL ROBIN, IS THE KIND OF THING I'D EXPECT TO SEE, PROBABLY.

SO, I WOULDN'T RULE IT *OUT*...BUT AT THE SAME TIME, THIS *COULD* JUST BE A KID WHO'S INTO SPORTS.

WHICH PROBABLY DOESN'T HELP YOU *AT ALL*, DOES IT?

NOT REALLY, NO.

DID YOU RUN HIS PRINTS?

YOU THINK HE'S GOT A *CRIMINAL RECORD*?

HE'S DENSE TONIGHT, ISN'T HE?

HE HASN'T BEEN GETTING ANY LATELY. IT BOTHERS HIM.

HEY!

SHE'S TALKING ABOUT *CHILD REGISTRATION*, MARCUS. IT'S BECOMING MORE AND MORE COMMON THE PAST FEW YEARS.

LET'S JUST SEE IF OUR LITTLE ROBIN'S PARENTS ARE AMONG THE SCARED PARENTS CONTINGENT...

AND, WHAT DO YOU KNOW...?

OH, YOU HAVE *GOT* TO BE *KIDDING* ME...

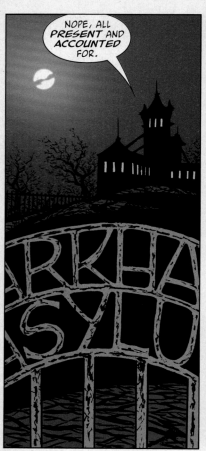

NOPE, ALL **PRESENT** AND **ACCOUNTED** FOR.

YOU'RE **SURE?**

DID THE **HEAD COUNT** AT **SHIFT** CHANGE, THAT WAS FOUR HOURS AGO.

WE'RE GOING TO WANT TO **CHECK** ON THE INMATES ANYWAY.

THAT, UH... WE'D **RATHER** YOU DIDN'T **DISTURB** THEM.

YOU MEAN **MORE** THAN THEY **ALREADY** ARE?

IT'S JUST...THE **POLICE** ARE **DISRUPTIVE,** THEY TEND TO **AGITATE** THE **INMATES.**

THE **INMATES** AREN'T THE ONLY ONES GOING TO BE **AGITATED,** DIRECTOR MCKENNA.

ARKHAM'S **REVOLVING** DOOR DOESN'T GIVE YOU A LOT OF ROOM TO **MANEUVER** HERE.

ESCAPES ARE **DOWN** FORTY-SEVEN PERCENT--

ALL IT TAKES IS **ONE.**

LOOK, DETECTIVE... ALLEN, RIGHT? WE'VE BEEN HAVING A...**HARD** NIGHT.

EXPLAIN.

I, UH... I'M NOT SURE I CAN.

WE DO BED-CHECKS EVERY HOUR, UNDERSTAND...

...SOMETIME BETWEEN THE ONE-THIRTY AND TWO-THIRTY CHECKS, SOMETHING... HAPPENED...

...THE INMATES, A LOT OF THEM, WELL...

...THEY STARTED PRESENTING INJURIES. BRUISING, MOSTLY. SOME BLEEDING, A COUPLE BLACK EYES.

A COUPLE MORE SERIOUS.

SERIOUS HOW?

WELL, JOKER HAS A BROKEN ARM.

BATMAN?

BATMAN.

HELL.

MAXIMUM SECURITY WARD
PROCEED WITH CAUTION
DO NOT SPEAK WITH THE INMATES

I PROMISE YOU, NONE OF OUR STAFF IS RESPONSIBLE--

NO, WE KNOW.

THIS IS GONNA BE FUN.

WASTE OF #$%ING *TIME*, MAN.

NO, WE *LEARNED* SOME *THINGS.*

WHAT, *ASIDE* FROM THE FACT THAT *TWO-FACE* STILL HAS A *THING* FOR RENEE?

SHUT UP, TOMMY.

SON OF A *BITCH!*

SON OF A *BITCH!*

EASY, PARTNER!

DON'T *TELL* ME EASY!

WE'RE DOING THIS *AGAIN,* RENEE! *AGAIN,* IT'S THE *SAME* THING, *OVER* AND *OVER!*

CHASING *BATMAN.*

WE'RE *ALWAYS* CHASING BATMAN.

YOU SEE THIS?

Gotham Gazette

EXTRA

IS ROBIN DEAD?

ONLY IN *GOTHAM* WOULD THEY PUT OUT AN *EXTRA* IN THE MIDDLE OF THE GODDAMN NIGHT.

BARS DON'T CLOSE 'TIL *FOUR*, CAPTAIN...EVERY DRUNK IN THE CITY'LL BE READING THIS ON THE SUBWAY HOME.

I KNOW IT.

BUT WHAT I'D *LIKE* TO KNOW IS HOW THE HELL THE GAZETTE GOT A HOLD OF OUR *CRIME SCENE* PHOTO.

YOU'RE NOT STILL GOING TO DEFEND *CORRIGAN*, ARE YOU, JOSIE?

NO...I'M NOT.

YOU DON'T KNOW HOW HARD I'M TRYING TO GET THAT MAN *FIRED*.

WELL, IF YOU'RE LOOKING FOR SOME *GOOD* NEWS, CAP, WE'VE GOT AN I.D. ON OUR VIC.

HOW?

THE MAGIC OF NATIONAL PARANOIA AND CRAZES...

CHILD REGISTRATION.

YES SIR... TURNS OUT OUR VIC IS ONE *ROGER BAUMBACH*, THE ONLY CHILD OF A FAMILY FROM THE PARK ROW AREA.

BUT ACCORDING TO RECORDS THEY'VE ONLY LIVED IN THE CITY LITTLE OVER A YEAR, SO THERE'S NO WAY THIS KID IS THE REAL ROBIN.

NO ONE WANTS THAT TO BE TRUE MORE THAN ME, DETECTIVE, BUT WE CAN'T MAKE THAT ASSUMPTION.

AS OUR FRIEND SIMON LIPPMAN SO ELOQUENTLY POINTS OUT IN THIS ARTICLE, WE HAVE NO WAY OF KNOWING THAT THERE'S ONLY ONE ROBIN TO BEGIN WITH.

WHAT, SO ROBIN'S LIKE LASSIE?

WE DON'T KNOW, THAT'S WHAT I'M SAYING, AND UNTIL WE DO, YOU NEED TO GO TALK TO THE PARENTS OF THE DECEASED...

AND TOMORROW WE'VE GOT TO GET ROBIN'S KNOWN ASSOCIATES IN HERE FOR QUESTIONING.

YOU'RE GOING TO HAUL IN A BUNCH OF TEENAGE SUPER HEROES? HOW YOU PLANNING TO PULL THAT ONE OFF, CAPTAIN?

I'VE GOT MY WAYS...

NOW GO WAKE THE BAUMBACHS UP WITH THE BAD NEWS AND SEE WHAT THEY'VE GOT TO SAY.

YES SIR, MA'AM...

LOIS... SORRY TO WAKE YOU. IT'S MAGGIE SAWYER, CALLING FROM GOTHAM.

YEAH, I KNOW, SORRY... BUT I NEED A FAVOR...

NOW LISTEN, TAKAHATA...I KNOW THIS IS THE PENGUIN'S PLACE, AND HE'S A TOTAL SCUMBAG...BUT LEGALLY, THIS PLACE IS LEGIT.

ICEBERG LOUNGE

SO DON'T GO IN THERE WAVING YOUR GUN AROUND. THIS ISN'T SOME NARCO BUST.

I DID THAT **ONE TIME**, CHANDLER, FOUR **MONTHS** AGO. THINK YOU MIGHT LET IT **DROP** SOMEDAY?

SOMEDAY.

MAYBE.

ANYWAY, I THOUGHT PENGUIN WAS OPERATING OUT OF BLÜDHAVEN THESE DAYS?

HE IS, BUT HE'S STILL GOT THE **ICEBERG**, SO HE'S BACK IN GOTHAM ALL THE TIME. JUST LIKES TO KEEP IT QUIET.

MY SNITCH SAYS HE'S IN TOWN THIS WEEKEND, SO...

SEEMS TO BE THE **PROBLEM**, OFFICERS?

HERE TO SEE COBBLEPOT.

YOU GOT A WARRANT?

THIS'S A **NIGHTCLUB** DURING STANDARD OPERATING HOURS, JARHEAD, WE DON'T **NEED** ONE.

LEMME CALL AHEAD, ANYWAY.

WHATEVER TURNS YOU ON.

26

#£%!

HEY!

ROMY...LET ME SEE--

LEAVE IT! I'B FINE!

...SHIZ... BY GUN...

WHAT?

THAD BASSARD TOOK BY GUN...

31

HE TOOK HER **WEAPON?**

SO FAST **NONE** OF US EVEN **SAW** IT.

ONE SECOND ROMY'S **STANDING,** THE **NEXT** SHE'S **GUSHING** BLOOD FROM HER **NOSE** AND HER **HANDS** ARE **EMPTY.**

WHY WOULD HE TAKE HER **PIECE?**

LIKE I'M AN **EXPERT** ON **BATMAN** ALL OF THE SUDDEN?

MY OLD **BEAT,** IF WE EVEN **HEARD** ABOUT HIM, HE WAS **ALREADY** GONE, YOU KNOW?

YEAH, BUT SEE, THAT'S **NOT** THE KIND OF **THING** HE DOES, TAKING A **POLICE'S** WEAPON, NOT EVEN AS THINGS **STAND** RIGHT NOW.

NOT **UNLESS** SOMEONE'S **DRAWING** DOWN ON HIM, SEE WHAT I'M **SAYING?**

I DON'T **KNOW,** BURKE...IT **HAPPENED** REALLY **FAST,** ALL RIGHT?

HEY, MARCUS. GET ANYTHING FROM **ROBIN'S** PARENTS?

FOUR IN THE **MORNING** WHEN WE **BROKE** THE NEWS, THE **BAUMBACHS** WERE PRETTY **RATTLED.**

JO AND I ARE HEADING BACK TO TALK TO THEM **AGAIN.**

LET CRIS AND ME KNOW IF WE CAN **HELP.**

SHE'S YOUR **PARTNER,** NOOB.

BACK HER **UP.**

...PRELIMINARY FROM THE *LAB,* AND IT'S *EXACTLY* WHAT YOU'D *EXPECT.*

TELL ME WE'RE KEEPING *CORRIGAN* OFF THIS ONE.

DOING *EVERY-THING* WE *CAN,* RENEE, BUT YOU *KNOW* HOW IT *IS* DOWN THERE.

--ANOTHER ONE OFF THE *TIP* LINE, THIS GUY CLAIMING THAT *HE'S* THE *REAL* ROBIN...

...AND THAT HE'S FEELING JUST *FINE,* THANKS FOR OUR *CONCERN...*

HEY, PARTNER. READY TO *ROLL?*

HMM?

SURE, YEAH.

LET'S VISIT *MORE* MISERY ON THE *GRIEVING* PARENTS.

IT'S OUR *JOB,* MARCUS. THEY'LL *THANK* US WHEN WE *CATCH* THE S.O.B. WHO *WHACKED* THEIR *SON.*

CAPTAIN DOESN'T *KNOW* THAT ROMY LOST HER *PIECE.*

YEAH, HOW LONG YOU FIGURE *THAT'S* GONNA *LAST?*

SHE TOOK A *SHOT* AT HIM, YOU *KNOW* SHE DID. NO *OTHER* REASON HE'D DO IT.

YOU'RE *STILL* TALKING LIKE HE'S INNOCENT--

LIPPMAN!!!

WHERE THE HELL IS SIMON LIPPMAN?

STACY!

HE WAS AROUND, I DON'T--

YOU *FIND* THAT *SON OF A BITCH* AND YOU GET HIM INTO *MY* OFFICE RIGHT *NOW.*

HE DOESN'T WORK FOR US, I MEAN, HE'S PROBABLY AT--

NOW, STACY!

CAPTAIN?

YOU *SEE* THIS? HE DID IT *AGAIN!* WHERE THE HELL IS HE *GETTING* THESE FROM?

NONE OF US HAVE *TALKED* TO HIM, HE *CAN'T* HAVE LEAKED--

NOT US!

CLASSIFIEDS

THE C.S.U., HE'S GOT SOME-ONE IN THE C.S.U., CORRIGAN OR ONE OF HIS *WINGED MONKEYS*--

--THEY'RE LEAKING THE *CRIME SCENE* PHOTOS, THIS IS THE *SECOND* DAMN ONE!

Sidekick on the sidewalk - Did Batman

I'LL *KILL* HIM, I SWEAR I'LL--

UHMM... CAN I...

...CAN I *HELP* YOU?

HOPE SO.

WE'RE HERE TO **SPEAK** WITH A CAPTAIN MARGARET SAWYER?

THAT'D BE **ME**, I'M CAPTAIN SAWYER.

CYBORG, RIGHT?

THAT'S CORRECT.

YOU WANTED TO **ASK** US SOME **QUESTIONS** ABOUT **ROBIN**?

YES. I ASSUME ONE OF YOU HAS **GUARDIAN** STATUS FOR THE **MINORS**?

BOTH MYSELF AND GAR. I CAN **GIVE** YOU THE **FILES** IF YOU **NEED** THEM.

I WILL. WE'LL **CONDUCT** THE **INTERVIEWS** TWO AT A **TIME**, THEN--

IS THIS **REALLY** NECESSARY? ROBIN IS **ALIVE** AND **WELL**.

I'M AFRAID IT **IS**.

YOU **WON'T** TAKE OUR **WORD** FOR IT?

YOU GOING TO **GIVE** ME ROBIN'S **REAL** NAME?

NO? DIDN'T **THINK** SO.

DEL ARRAZIO, BARTLETT, IF YOU TWO WILL **ESCORT** KID FLASH AND **BEAST BOY** INTO INTERVIEW ONE, PLEASE...

--JUST SAYING, MARCUS, IT WAS ME, I'D HOPE MY BOYFRIEND WOULD SAY A FEW WORDS.

WHAT AM I SUPPOSED TO SAY?

"SORRY BATMAN TOOK YOUR GUN, BUT YOU STILL HAVE YOUR BACKUP, RIGHT?"

SHE'S PROBABLY FEELING LIKE ♯#%⁰ IS ALL I'M SAYING.

HOW 'BOUT WE JUST CONCENTRATE ON OUR CASE, INSTEAD OF BUSTING MY HUMP FOR BEING A BAD BOYFRIEND?

WE'VE GOTTA TRY AND GET SOMETHING USEFUL OUT OF THE VIC'S PARENTS AND I, FOR ONE--

OH, YOU HAVE GOT TO BE ♯#%⁰ING ME.

--THAT YOUR SON WAS THE REAL ROBIN?

IN LIGHT OF INFORMATION FROM THE POLICE, WE BELIEVE HE WAS. OR AT LEAST, THAT HE WAS A ROBIN. WE CAN'T KNOW IF HE WAS THE ONLY ONE.

WE THOUGHT ROGER WAS OUT LATE NIGHTS PRACTICING GYMNASTICS, AND LATELY HE'D GOTTEN INTERESTED IN THEATER, HE CLAIMED...

...BUT NOW IT'S CLEAR TO US THAT HE WAS COVERING FOR HIS SECRET LIFE.

--WAS IN FACT ROBIN, DO YOU BLAME BATMAN FOR HIS DEATH, OR--

WHY ARE YOU NOT IN PROTECTIVE CUSTODY?

DO YOU BELIEVE THE JOKER KILLED YOUR SON?

DO YOU KNOW WHO BATMAN IS?

OKAY, FOLKS, G.C.P.D. LET'S *BREAK* THIS UP.

WE'VE STILL GOT TO TAKE THESE PEOPLE'S *STATEMENTS*.

YOU CAN'T *DISPERSE* US, DETECTIVE. WE WERE *INVITED*...

HOW ABOUT *THIS*, THEN?

YOU CAN ALL GET THE HELL OUT OF HERE, OR I CAN CALL SOME *UNIS* DOWN TO BOOK EVERY ONE OF YOU FOR INTER- FERING WITH AN ACTIVE *HOMICIDE* INVESTIGATION.

THAT'LL NEVER STICK.

BUT IT'LL RUIN YOUR DAY.

NAZI.

BITE ME.

LET IT *GO*, JEFF... JUST GOT A CALL FROM A *SOURCE* AT CENTRAL. THE *TEEN TITANS* JUST WALKED IN.

REALLY? NEED A RIDE, DUNNING?

UH... WERE WE NOT *SUPPOSED* TO TALK TO THE *PRESS?*

YOU DIDN'T SAY ANYTHING ABOUT THAT *LAST NIGHT*, DETECTIVES...

BECAUSE WE *DIDN'T* THINK WE'D *NEED*--

LET'S ALL JUST GO INSIDE AND TALK... *PLEASE.*

--BUT LAST NIGHT YOU DIDN'T WANT TO TALK, AND THIS MORNING WE FIND YOU HOLDING COURT WITH THE *MEDIA*.

WELL, LAST NIGHT...IT WAS JUST...HOW ARE YOU SUPPOSED TO REACT TO...?

DON'T YOU *DARE* JUDGE US, DETECTIVE. IF WE WANT TO SHARE OUR GRIEF WITH THIS CITY, THAT'S OUR BUSINESS.

LET'S NOT FORGET WHO LOST THEIR ONLY CHILD LAST NIGHT.

I HAVEN'T *FORGOTTEN*, MR. BAUMBACH.

BUT YOU'RE OUT THERE TELLING THE WHOLE WORLD YOUR SON WAS *ROBIN*. DO YOU *REALIZE* THE DANGER THAT COULD PUT YOU IN?

WHAT ARE YOU *TALKING* ABOUT?

TWO WORDS FOR YOU--*THE JOKER.*

OH...OH *GOD*...

SO, WAIT...YOU *DON'T* THINK THAT ROGER *WAS* ROBIN? THE GAZETTE SAID THERE MAY BE MORE THAN *ONE*, SO WE THOUGHT--

WE DON'T KNOW, HONESTLY, MRS. BAUMBACH, BUT WE'RE LEANING TOWARDS *NOT*.

OH...BUT THEN, WHY WOULD HE BE WEARING THAT *OUTFIT*...?

THAT'S WHAT WE'RE TRYING TO *FIND* OUT.

NOW, IF WE COULD JUST GET SOME *DETAILS* ABOUT ROGER'S *ACTIVITIES*... YOU MENTIONED *GYMNASTICS* CLASSES...

...THE LAST TIME YOU *SAW* HIM?

SUNDAY *NIGHT*, WHEN WE WERE *ALL* LEAVING THE TOWER.

YOU KNOW WHERE HE WAS *HEADED*?

BLÜDHAVEN, I THINK. I MEAN, I *DON'T* ACTUALLY *KNOW* WHERE HE *LIVES* THESE DAYS.

THESE DAYS?

ROBIN'S HAD A...*ROUGH* YEAR, DETECTIVE PROCJNOW...

...THERE'S BEEN A *LOT* FOR HIM TO *DEAL* WITH.

I DON'T REALLY *KNOW* HIM THAT WELL, TO BE *HONEST*, DETECTIVE CROWE.

I'M *STILL* PRETTY *NEW* TO THE *TEAM*.

IS THERE *ANYTHING* YOU *CAN* TELL US?

NOTHING YOU *WANT* TO *HEAR*.

BUT IF YOU GIVE US *TEN* MINUTES, THE TITANS WILL *SOLVE* THIS CRIME *FOR* YOU.

BECAUSE THE *BOY* YOU *FOUND* IS *NOT* ROBIN.

THAT'S A *NICE* OFFER, MS. RAVEN, BUT--

EXCUSE ME, IS THIS THE *M.C.U.*?

I'M NOT **OFFICIALLY** WITH THE TITANS AT THE MOMENT, BUT I WAS **HOPING** I COULD **HELP,** YOU UNDERSTAND.

UHM... YES...UH...

OVER HERE, STARFIRE.

I HAVE BEEN **TRYING** TO **EXPLAIN** THAT **ROBIN** IS **ALIVE** AND **WELL.**

AND IF THESE **CIVIL SERVICE** BUREAUCRATS WOULD ONLY **LET** US, WE COULD **SOLVE** THIS **CASE** FOR THEM.

I SEE...

...PERHAPS I CAN BE **MORE** PERSUASIVE, RAVEN?

MEN.

YOU THINK?

WOW.

YOU SHOULD SEE WONDER WOMAN.

HOLY #$%&.

WHERE ARE THE *REST* OF THEM?

SIMON LIPPMAN.

WOULD YOU *JOIN* ME IN MY OFFICE PLEASE, MR. *LIPPMAN?*

BE MY *PLEASURE* TO, CAPTAIN SAWYER.

IS SHE ACTUALLY *GLOWING* OR IS THAT MY *IMAGINATION?*

SHE'S ACTUALLY *GLOWING.*

MONTOYA, YOU'RE *DROOLING.*

SHOVE IT, SIMON.

THE TEEN TITANS IN THE M.C.U. SQUADROOM.

YOU LET A *CAMERA* CREW UP HERE, YOU COULD MAKE A LOT OF FRIENDS IN THE *PRESS,* CAPTAIN.

SHUT UP.

WHAT?

WHO GAVE IT TO YOU?

WHAT ARE YOU *TALKING* ABOUT?

Gotham Gazette
BOY WONDER, STREET PIZZA

I'M *NOT* IN THE *MOOD*, SIMON! WHERE THE *HELL* DID YOU GET THE *PHOTO*?

NICE SHOT.

DON'T GET *CUTE* WITH ME!

THAT'S A DAMN *CRIME SCENE PHOTO*, SIMON, IT'S *POLICE PROPERTY*, AND IT HAS *BEARING* ON AN *ONGOING* INVESTIGATION!

I WANT TO KNOW *WHERE* YOU GOT IT, I WANT TO KNOW *WHO* GAVE IT TO YOU.

AND I WANT TO KNOW *RIGHT NOW.*

GAZETTE

I'M *NOT* GOING TO GIVE UP A *SOURCE*, CAPTAIN.

WAS IT *CORRIGAN*? IS *THAT* WHO IT *WAS*?

DID HE *OFFER* TO *SELL* IT TO YOU? IS *THAT* WHAT HAPPENED?

YOU *CAN'T* SERIOUSLY EXPECT ME TO *ANSWER* THAT.

YES, I *CAN*.

I'VE *TREATED* YOU *WELL*, SIMON, I'VE GIVEN YOU *ACCESS* THAT OTHER REPORTERS ONLY *DREAM* ABOUT. YOU *OWE* ME.

NOT *THIS* MUCH, I *DON'T*.

SO IT MEANS *NOTHING?* ALL THE FAVORS I'VE DONE FOR YOU, THEY MEAN *NOTHING?*

CAPTAIN, YOU *CAN'T* ASK ME TO GIVE UP A *SOURCE!*

THINK ABOUT HOW MANY *TIMES* I'VE QUOTED YOU OR THE *OTHER* DETECTIVES *ANONYMOUSLY.*

IF I *RAT* THE *SOURCE,* NO ONE *EVER* TRUSTS ME *AGAIN.*

I CAN'T DO IT.

...C'MON...

...MAGGIE, GIVE ME A *BREAK* HERE--

GET OUT.

MAGGIE--

GET *OUT* OF MY SQUADROOM, SIMON.

SLAM

BASTARD.

CAN YOU *SEE* THEM? CAN *ANYONE--*

DETECTIVES! DETECTIVES!!

... WITH NO SIGNS OF *SUPERBOY,* ISN'T YOUR STATEMENT A LITTLE *DISINGENUOUS?*

--IF IT *WAS* STARFIRE, THEN IT'S THE *OUTSIDERS,* SO *LOOK* FOR--

DID THE BAUMBACHS HAVE ANY *FURTHER* COMMENT--

--ASK AT WONDER *RL* ANSWER A *FEW* QUESTIONS FOR US?

LIPPMAN!

IS IT *TRUE?* THE TEEN TITANS ARE UP THERE?

THEY *WERE,* ALL OF THEM BUT *SUPERBOY.* THEY JUST *LEFT* FROM THE *ROOF.*

NO *BATMAN,* THOUGH, HUH?

GET *REAL.*

YOU *OKAY,* MAN? YOU LOOK LIKE YOUR *DOG* DIED.

SAWYER JUST BUSTED MY *CHOPS* ABOUT THE *FRONT PAGE* OF THE *GAZETTE.* SHE THINKS THE PHOTOS ARE *MY* FAULT.

WANTED ME TO GIVE UP MY *SOURCE.*

THE PHOTOS *DIDN'T* COME FROM YOU, THOUGH. DID THEY?

I DON'T *KNOW* WHERE THE PHOTOS CAME FROM.

SO YOU JUST *TELL* HER THAT. NO *PROBLEM.*

THAT'S NOT THE *POINT,* DUNNING. SHE *NEVER* SHOULD HAVE *ASKED* FOR MY SOURCE.

IT'S THE *PRINCIPLE* OF THE THING.

HEY, DRIVER, YOU ACTUALLY TELL JEFF BRAXTON FROM W.B.G.K. TO *SUCK IT?*

WAY TO DEAL WITH THE PRESS.

THAT'S *NOT* WHAT I SAID...

...I TOLD HIM TO *BITE ME.*

WHICH I'M SURE WILL LOOK *MUCH BETTER* ON THE EVENING NEWS.

HELL, EVEN IF SAWYER PUTS YOU ON HER &#&%-LIST, YOU'LL STILL BE IN *SECOND* POSITION *TODAY,* MARCUS...

NICE, COHEN. VERY DECENT OF YOU.

WHAT?

ROMY... *WAIT...*

SO, WHAT HAPPENED WITH THE PARENTS? GET ANYTHING ON OUR VIC?

HE'S DEFINITELY *NOT* ROBIN. CONFIRMED THE KID WAS TAKING *GYMNASTICS* AND *ACTING* LESSONS FIVE NIGHTS A WEEK, JUST LIKE HE TOLD HIS FOLKS.

HIS TEACHERS WERE *DEVASTATED,* ONE OF THEM SAID HE COULD'VE GONE TO THE *OLYMPICS,* MAYBE.

SO, WE GOT A KID WHO'S **NOT** ROBIN SHOVED OFF A ROOF, OR WHO MISSED HIS JUMP.

WHAT A WORLD.

YOU SAID IT.

JUST SAY IT, MARCUS. I **SCREWED** UP.

I JUST WANT TO SEE IF YOU'RE ALL RIGHT. I DON'T **CARE** IF YOU SCREWED UP.

OF **COURSE** I'M NOT ALL RIGHT. BATMAN STOLE MY FRIGGING **GUN** AND BROKE MY **NOSE.**

YOU GONNA TELL THE CAPTAIN ABOUT YOUR PIECE?

NOT LIKE I'VE GOT MUCH **CHOICE,** IS IT?

DID YOU SHOOT AT HIM? IS **THAT** WHY?

HIS REASONS DON'T **MATTER,** DO THEY? HE **ASSAULTED** AN OFFICER.

SURE, BUT... **JESUS,** ROMY... THAT'S NOT GOING TO LOOK GOOD TO THE BRASS.

NOT AFTER WHAT HAPPENED WITH NATE.

YOU MEAN AFTER BATMAN GOT HIM **KILLED?**

YEAH. IT'S GONNA LOOK LIKE YOU'RE OUT FOR REVENGE.

AND I KNOW YOU **HATE** THE GUY... BUT YOU GOTTA KNOW THAT **WHATEVER** THE PRESENT SITUATION...

"...AT THE END OF THE DAY, HE'S ON **OUR** SIDE, IN HIS OWN WAY."

HEY...

OH, MY GOD...

HI.

STACY, RIGHT?

YEAH...?

CAN YOU TELL THEM IT WASN'T **ME** THAT GOT KILLED?

YEAH, BUT--WELL, THEY'D REALLY LIKE TO TALK WITH YOU. I MEAN, THEY...

I CAN'T.

THERE ARE RULES.

WHY **NOT?**

BATMAN'S RULES?

SORT OF, YEAH.

CAN YOU DO ME A *FAVOR*, THEN?

I CAN TRY. WHAT?

CAN YOU GET DETECTIVE CHANDLER'S GUN BACK FROM HIM?

SHE'S GOING TO GET IN *A LOT* OF TROUBLE, AND SHE'S REALLY REALLY *NICE*, SHE'S JUST BEEN, UM, KINDA *MAD* AT BATMAN, SINCE HER *PARTNER* GOT KILLED...

YOU KNOW, IN THAT WHOLE *JOKER* THING AT THE *TOY STORE*?

DETECTIVE NATE PATTON.

YOU *KNOW* HIS NAME?

OF COURSE I KNOW HIS NAME.

WAIT...

BATMAN *TOOK* HER WEAPON?

YEAH, BUT... WELL, I THINK SHE KINDA...UM...SHE MIGHT'VE...

...SHOT HIM?

I REALLY MISS THE OLD DAYS.

ME, TOO. REALLY.

49

I CAN'T BELIEVE YOU JUST SAID THAT TO ME...

...I THOUGHT *YOU* HATED BATMAN MORE THAN ANYONE HERE...NOW YOU THINK HE'S ON *OUR SIDE*?

I NEVER HATED HIM. I JUST HATED...I GUESS I HATED THAT WE *NEEDED* HIM.

HATED THAT THIS CITY IS SO SCREWED UP THAT IT NEEDS MORE THAN POLICE SOMETIMES.

NO, AFTER THAT THING WITH *FREEZE*, YOU -- YOU HATED HIM.

MY *PARTNER* WAS DEAD, I WAS ANGRY...BUT I GOT OVER IT, ROMY.

YOU *HELPED ME* DO THAT.

AND IT TEARS ME UP TO SEE YOU LIKE THIS...YOU SEEM FINE, BUT AS SOON AS THE BAT ENTERS THE PICTURE, YOU JUST...GO OVER *THE EDGE*.

I KNOW. I CAN'T HELP IT.

HEY, SORRY TO BREAK THE CIRCLE OF TRUST HERE, BUT WE CAUGHT ANOTHER BODY...

ANOTHER BODY?

YEP, ANOTHER *ROBIN.*

--SAY HE'D BEEN IN THE WATER APPROXIMATELY TEN HOURS, GIVE OR TAKE.

DON'T TELL ME THIS ONE DROWNED?

NO. PETECHIAL HEMORRHAGES IN BOTH EYES. HE WAS SUFFOCATED SOMEHOW BEFORE HE HIT THE WATER.

DEAD ROBIN PART THREE OF FOUR

THIS DOESN'T *FIT*, MARCUS. OUR KILLER JUST SNUFFS THIS KID AND DUMPS HIM OFF A *BRIDGE*?

THE FIRST BODY WAS IN *PLAIN SIGHT*. THIS ONE COULD'VE DRIFTED OUT TO SEA.

NO. HARBOR CAPTAIN SAID HE WAS FLOATING IN A *REGULAR PATROL ROUTE*, WITH NO ANCHOR TO PULL HIM UNDER...

...SO, IT'S REALLY MORE OF A SHOCK THEY DIDN'T FIND HIM *SOONER*.

REAL QUESTION IS: WHAT'S OUR PERP *THINKING*? ONE DEAD KID IN A ROBIN SUIT, THAT COULD BE *ANYTHING*, RIGHT? ACCIDENT, SUICIDE, WHO KNOWS...?

BUT TWO KIDS, **BOTH** IN THESE EXPENSIVE OUTFITS...BOTH KILLED WITHIN **A DAY** OF EACH OTHER?

HEY, REINER, ANY SIGN OF SEXUAL ASSAULT ON THIS ONE?

SORRY TO DISAPPOINT, DETECTIVE.

SEE, THAT'S JUST... WEIRD.

YOU'D BE **MORE COMFORTABLE** IF OUR PERP WAS MOLESTING THE VICS?

HELL YES...AT LEAST **THAT** I'VE SEEN.

THIS IS JUST... NUTS.

IS IT JUST ME, OR DOES THAT KID LOOK FAMILIAR?

WELL, WE **DID** JUST HAVE ONE OF THESE **YESTERDAY**, REMEMBER?

HA HA...

NO, SERIOUSLY... I'VE SEEN THIS KID BEFORE SOME- WHERE.

AH, #¢$%IN' HELL...

LOOKS LIKE SOMEONE ALREADY ALERTED THE FRIGGING MEDIA ON US.

CHRIST, CAPTAIN SAWYER'S GONNA BE **THRILLED**...

MOTHER*%$¢!

MOTHER*%$¢!
MOTHER*%$¢!
MOTHER*%$¢!

BRRING

BRRING BRRING

CAPTAIN! THE *PHONES* WON'T *STOP* RINGING!

I'VE GOT *KLEX* HERE, THEY WANT TO KNOW IF WE CAN *CONFIRM* A *SECOND DEAD ROBIN* --

NO *%$#ING COMMENT!

EVERYONE GOT THAT?

YES, MA'AM.

YES, CAPTAIN.

GOT IT.

YES'M.

54

FREEDOM OF THE PRESS IS A BASIC RIGHT, A TENET ON WHICH OUR NATION IS BUILT FREEDOM OF THE PRESS IS A BASIC RIGHT --

MIKE!

MAGGIE, IF YOU'RE ABOUT TO TELL ME WE'VE CAUGHT A SECOND ONE...

HELL YEAH! ROBIN NUMBER TWO JUST BOBBED TO THE SURFACE OF THE SPRANG RIVER!

BUT DON'T FEEL BAD IF YOU'RE MISSING THE DETAILS, COMMISSIONER...

...IT'LL BE ON THE NEWS AT ELEVEN.

HOW'D THE PRESS GET IT SO QUICK?

TWO DOZEN WAYS AT LEAST, YOU KNOW THAT. THERE'RE ANY NUMBER OF PEOPLE IN THIS DEPARTMENT WHO'D BE HAPPY TO LEAK INFORMATION FOR CASH OR JUST TO $€#% WITH US.

THAT SAID, I'M PERSONALLY BLAMING SIMON LIPPMAN.

I'LL CALL EDWARDS IN MEDIA, GET ANOTHER PRESS CONFERENCE SCHEDULED IMMEDIATELY.

YOU'LL HAVE TO JOIN ME FOR IT.

I'LL TRY TO KEEP MY LUNCH DOWN.

COMMISSIONER! COMMISSIONER!

--CONFIRM YOU *RECEIVED* A CALL FROM THE *RIDDLER* CLAIMING RESPONSIBILITY?

--IDENTITY OF *BOTH* ROBINS AND THEIR *CONNECTION* TO THE BATMAN--

--THAT YOU IN *FACT* HAVE *NO* LEADS AND *NOTHING* TO GO ON?

--RUMORS THAT *STARFIRE* WAS *STRIP-SEARCHED* PRIOR TO--

ALL RIGHT, LET'S SEE IF WE CAN ACT LIKE *HUMAN BEINGS* AND NOT A PACK OF *FRENZIED HYENAS,* SHALL WE?

A LITTLE OVER AN *HOUR* AGO A *SECOND* YOUNG MAN *DRESSED* IN *IDENTICAL* FASHION AND *COSTUME* AS THE *FIRST* WAS PULLED FROM THE SPRANG...

...M.C.U. DETECTIVES ARE *STILL* PROCESSING THE *SCENE,* AND ARE *TREATING* THIS AS A *RELATED* HOMICIDE.

WE EXPECT INITIAL *AUTOPSY* RESULTS WITHIN THE NEXT TWO HOURS, AT WHICH TIME WE'LL BE ISSUING A *SECOND* STATEMENT.

I'LL TAKE *THREE* QUESTIONS, SO *MAKE* THEM *GOOD.*

WHY HAVEN'T THE *POLICE* BROUGHT *BATMAN* IN FOR *QUESTIONING?*

WHO SAYS WE *HAVEN'T?*

NEXT QUESTION...

FAASH

I SEE WHAT YOU MEAN, JOSIE...HE **DOES** LOOK SOMEWHAT FAMILIAR.

HE LOOKS JUST LIKE THE **OTHER** KID.

NO...THERE'S SOMETHING ABOUT HIS EYEBROWS...

DUDE, IT'S YOUR **BREATH.**

WHAT THE #&$% DID YOU JUST SAY TO ME?

NOT YOU, **HIM.** THAT'S THE KID FROM THE **MIGHTY MINTS** ADS LAST YEAR, REMEMBER?

DUDE, IT'S YOUR **BREATH!**

...BUT NOTHING MORE ON THE SECOND BODY?

--HEY! HEY, THAT'S WHY I'M ASKING YOU, DAMMIT!

GO TO HELL.

DUNNING!

HEY, SIMON.

GIVE ME THE BULLET, WHAT'D I MISS?

IT WAS WHAT YOU'D EXPECT, MAN, NOTHING NEW.

AKINS CONFIRMS THAT A SECOND BOY WAS PULLED FROM THE RIVER, SAYS HE WAS DRESSED LIKE ROBIN.

THEY I.D. THE KID YET?

IF THEY HAVE, THEY WOULDN'T SAY.

LOOKS LIKE ONE OF THE BAT'S FREAKS IS AT WORK HERE, DRESSING UP KIDS AND OFFING THEM.

THAT IGNORES THE MULTIPLE ROBIN THEORY.

WHAT?

YOU LOOK AT THE HISTORIES, DUNNING, THERE'VE BEEN DIFFERENT KIDS INSIDE THAT SUIT, IT'S OBVIOUS.

HELL, APPARENTLY THERE WAS A GIRL WONDER A COUPLE MONTHS BACK.

YOU THINK THESE KIDS ARE THE **REAL** THING?

I'M SAYING IT'S **POSSIBLE.**

THING IS, THERE'S **NO** KNOWN **HISTORY** OF **MULTIPLE** ROBINS BEING ACTIVE AT THE **SAME** TIME.

C'MON, **TELL** ME. THEY SAY **ANYTHING** ELSE?

THEY HAVE ANY **SUSPECTS,** AT LEAST?

NOTHING, MAN. THEY'RE **STONEWALLED,** YOU CAN TELL.

SAWYER MUST **REALLY** WANT YOUR **HEAD** IN A **SACK** TO HAVE YOU EJECTED FROM THE **CONFERENCE** LIKE THAT.

YEAH, YOU **DON'T** WANT TO PISS HER **OFF.**

WHY DON'T YOU **JUST** TELL HER THE **PHOTOS** WEREN'T YOUR **FAULT?**

I ALREADY TOLD YOU, IT'S THE **PRINCIPLE.**

IT DOESN'T **BOTHER** ME THAT SHE **THINKS** I'M THE **LEAK,** DUNNING.

SHE GOT **BLINDSIDED,** SHE'S FEELING **BETRAYED,** I CAN SEE HOW SHE THINKS IT'S **ME.**

I CAN EVEN CUT HER **SLACK** FOR THAT.

BUT SHE **EXPECTED** ME TO GIVE UP A **SOURCE.**

SHE SHOULD **KNOW** ME BETTER THAN THAT BY **NOW,** Y'KNOW?

YOU'RE **OLD SCHOOL,** LIPPMAN, YOU KNOW THAT?

NO SCHOOL LIKE THE OLD SCHOOL, MAN.

HAVE A **NIGHT,** DUNNING.

YOU WANT ME TO *LET* YOU GUYS *INSIDE?*

I'VE GOT *KEYS* FOR JUST ABOUT *EVERY* OFFICE IN THE *BUILDING.*

IT'S ALL RIGHT, WE'VE GOT THE *OWNER* COMING DOWN.

YOU'RE *SURE?*

WE'RE *SURE.*

YEAH, *SUPPOSE* YOU'D NEED A *WARRANT* OR SOMETHING LIKE THAT, HUH?

WELL, YOU *NEED* ANYTHING, I'LL BE *DOWN* IN THE *LOBBY.*

SHINING EYES

THANKS, MISTER GERARD.

DING

YOU LOOK *BEAT.*

I *AM* BEAT.

WHAT'S GOING ON *BETWEEN* YOU AND *CORRIGAN?*

I *BEG* YOUR *PARDON?*

NOT LIKE *THAT.*

THEN LIKE *WHAT?*

I NEVER ASKED YOU HOW YOU CLEARED ME FOR THE LAMONICA SHOOT--

DING

I'M SORRY, I'M SORRY, I GOT HERE AS SOON AS I COULD--

--YOU'RE THE POLICE, YOU'RE THE DETECTIVES WHO CALLED ABOUT SCOTT BENJAMIN?

MISTER SWACK?

RIGHT, YES, FELIX SWACK.

DETECTIVE ALLEN, THIS IS DETECTIVE MONTOYA.

YOU REPPED SCOTT BENJAMIN FOR THE MIGHTY MINTS CAMPAIGN?

THAT AND HALF A DOZEN OTHER JOBS...

...NONE AS BIG AS THE M.M. ACCOUNT, OF COURSE.

VERY TALENTED KID, SCOTT. GREAT CHARISMA, WONDERFUL STAGE PRESENCE...

...COMPLETE MASTERY OF HIS INSTRUMENT, EVEN AT FIFTEEN.

INSTRUMENT?

HIS BODY, THE ACTOR'S TOOL. SCOTT WAS PROBABLY THE MOST TALENTED ADOLESCENT WE REPPED.

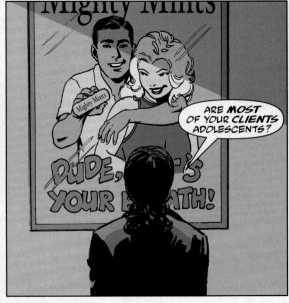

Mighty Mints

DUDE, YOUR BREATH!

Mighty Mints

ARE MOST OF YOUR CLIENTS ADOLESCENTS?

ROUGHLY *HALF*, I'D SAY.

ROGER BAUMBACH?

YOU KNOW *ROGER?*

MISTER SWACK, ROGER BAUMBACH WAS *MURDERED* NIGHT BEFORE *LAST.*

JESUS CHRIST.

WE'RE GOING TO NEED A *LIST* OF *ALL* YOUR *MALE* CLIENTS BETWEEN THE AGES OF THIRTEEN AND EIGHTEEN.

WE'RE GOING TO NEED THEIR *EMPLOYMENT* RECORDS, ALL *JOBS* OR *AUDITIONS* FOR THE LAST *SIX* MONTHS.

JESUS CHRIST.

THEY'RE JUST... THEY'RE JUST *KIDS*, DETECTIVE.

WE *REALLY* NEED THOSE *RECORDS*, MISTER SWACK.

THEY'RE... THEY'RE *THIS* WAY...

NO, DETECTIVE DRIVER AND JOSIE ARE WITH THE VICTIMS' *PARENTS*, RENEE, BUT THAT'S GOOD NEWS. LET ME TRANSFER YOU TO THE CAPTAIN... HOLD...

BRRNG

MAJOR CRIMES, HOW MAY I DIRECT YOUR CALL?

STACY?

YES...?

YOU KNOW WHO THIS IS. MEET ME ON THE ROOF.

HI...

HI...SORRY TO SURPRISE YOU LIKE THAT.

THAT'S ALL RIGHT...

I GOT IT BACK FOR YOU.

BACK...?

DETECTIVE CHANDLER'S WEAPON.

OH, RIGHT, THAT. I'M SORRY...IT'S BEEN A WEIRD WEEK.

YEAH, FOR ME TOO.

I CAN ONLY *IMAGINE*...

WELL, THANKS *SO* MUCH. THIS WILL SAVE ROMY A LOT OF TROUBLE.

DON'T WORRY ABOUT IT...BUT...

...HE SAID TO TELL HER *NOT* TO SHOOT HIM AGAIN.

I'M PRETTY SURE SHE *KNOWS.*

BUT, YOU KNOW...I'LL *TOTALLY* TELL HER, IF YOU THINK I SHOULD.

IT'S REALLY YOUR CALL. HE *DID* BREAK HER NOSE, RIGHT?

YEAH, I'LL JUST LET HER FIGURE IT OUT HERSELF, MAYBE...

SO...

HAS THERE BEEN ANY PROGRESS IN THE INVESTIGATION? I HEARD THE SECOND VICTIM WAS ALREADY IDENTIFIED?

YOU DID? WE JUST FOUND OUT ABOUT AN HOUR AGO...

OH, RIGHT... *BATMAN.*

SORRY.

WELL, SO, YEAH...THE SECOND VICTIM IS AN ACTOR, SCOTT BENJAMIN, AND IT TURNS OUT HE AND THE FIRST VICTIM WERE BOTH REPRESENTED BY THE SAME TALENT AGENCY...

...*SHINING EYES* OR SOMETHING LIKE THAT.

SO THEY'RE GOING OVER THE REST OF THE CLIENT LIST FOR BOYS THIRTEEN TO EIGHTEEN, HOPING TO FIND OUT MORE.

--CONNECTING ROGER BAUMBACH AND SCOTT BENJAMIN *THROUGH* THE SHINING EYES *TALENT* AGENCY.

THERE ARE SOME *TWO HUNDRED AND EIGHT* MALES BETWEEN THIRTEEN AND EIGHTEEN SHINING EYES CURRENTLY REPRESENTS.

WE'RE GOING TO HAVE TO *CHECK* THEM *ALL*, AND *PRONTO*.

WE LOOKING AT THIS FELIX SWACK AS A *SUSPECT?*

NAME LIKE *SWACK*, WE DAMN WELL *BETTER*.

TOMMY, *SHUT UP*.

NOT AT THE MOMENT.

THERE ARE STACKS OF RÉSUMÉS, HEAD SHOTS AND CONTACT INFO.

THEY *HAVEN'T* BEEN *SORTED*, SO IF YOU'VE GOT AN *OBVIOUS* NO-GO, HERE...

...THE **KID'S** OVERWEIGHT, FOR INSTANCE, JUST **DISREGARD.**

OTHERWISE, **START** MAKING CALLS.

UHM, EXCUSE ME...

...DETECTIVE CHANDLER?

HERE'S **HALF.**

THAT'S SO NOT **HALF,** YOU'RE GIVING ME THE **LION'S** SHARE.

DETECTIVE?

YOU'D BE A **GREAT** POLICE IF YOU STOPPED **COMPLAINING,** TAKA.

DETECTIVE CHANDLER?

TRYING TO **SOLVE** A **MURDER** HERE, STACY.

I JUST ...I...

WHAT?

...CALLING FROM THE M.C.U....

...GEOFF KIRKLAND, PLEASE?

...REGARDING AN INVESTIGATION...

...LEAVE A **MESSAGE?**

IT CAN WAIT.

--THIS CAN'T BE HAPPENING...

I KNOW, MRS. BENJAMIN... WE'LL HAVE A PATROL CAR TAKE YOU TO IDENTIFY THE BODY, JUST TO BE SURE.

BUT WE HAVE MATCHED SCOTT'S HEAD SHOT WITH OUR VICTIM. I'M SORRY.

OH, OH GOD...

IS YOUR HUSBAND HERE, MRS. BENJAMIN?

MY HUSBAND... NO...GARY MOVED TO CHICAGO AFTER THE DIVORCE...

OH, GOD, I HAVE TO CALL HIM...I HAVE TO TELL HIM.

I'M SORRY TO HAVE TO ASK YOU THESE QUESTIONS RIGHT NOW, MA'AM, BUT TIME IS OF THE ESSENCE HERE.

DO YOU KNOW OF ANY REASON WHY SCOTT WOULD BE WEARING A ROBIN COSTUME?

WHAT? NO... OF COURSE NOT.

WAS HE FRIENDS WITH ROGER BAUMBACH? DID THEY KNOW EACH OTHER?

NO, I DON'T KNOW...OH, GOD...SCOTT...WHO WOULD DO THIS?

WE'RE TRYING TO FIND THAT OUT, MRS. BENJAMIN.

WOULD YOU MIND IF WE SEARCHED SCOTT'S ROOM?

FINE, FINE... DO WHATEVER YOU WANT...

...MONTOYA, YES, RENEE MONTOYA...

...NO, I'D LIKE TO *SPEAK* WITH HIM IN *PERSON*...

...IF YOU COULD HAVE HIM *CALL* ME...

...NO, MA'AM, JORDAN'S *NOT* IN *TROUBLE*...

...I SWEAR--

--SON OF A *BITCH!*

UH, CRIS?

IT'S *NOT* THE SAME!

IT'S *NOT* THE *SAME DAMN PHOTO!*

THE *FRONT PAGE* PHOTO, RENEE...

...IT WAS TAKEN *BEFORE* WE GOT THERE, BEFORE WE STARTED *WORKING* THE *CRIME SCENE*...

...IT WAS TAKEN BY THE SON OF A BITCH WHO *KILLED* HIM...

HOLD UP...HERE'S A BUSINESS CARD WITH YESTERDAY'S DATE WRITTEN ON THE BACK, TOO.

WHAT? WHAT'S THE CARD?

YES MA'AM...NO. EXCUSE ME? NO, I WAS CALLING TO--

YOU DID? OKAY, HANG ON...LET ME GET YOUR ADDRESS, MA'AM.

OH...THIS...THIS IS...NO WAY...

WHAT?

HOT DAMN!

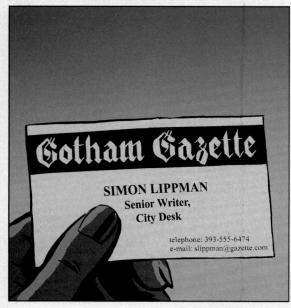

Gotham Gazette

SIMON LIPPMAN
Senior Writer,
City Desk

telephone: 393-555-6474
e-mail: slippman@gazette.com

WHAT IS IT, TAKA?

GET DRIVER AND JOSIE ON THE LINE...WE'VE GOT ANOTHER MISSING KID.

DOWN!

JESUS CHR--

GET DOWN ON THE GROUND!

NOW!

DEAD ROBIN
CONCLUSION

...RADIOED IT IN THAT THEY'VE GOT *LIPPMAN* IN *CUSTODY* AND ARE ON THE WAY HERE.

ASSUMING THAT HE'S *NOT* GOING TO GIVE IT UP--AND IT'S *GOTHAM*, SO I THINK WE ALL KNOW IT'S A *SAFE* ASSUMPTION-- THAT MEANS WE'VE GOT A *THIRD* KID OUT THERE SOMEWHERE.

KID'S NAME IS *ZACK WESTON*, SIXTEEN, FROM THE HEIGHTS.

DEL ARRAZIO AND *BARTLETT* ARE ON THEIR WAY TO *TALK* TO THE *PARENTS* AS WE SPEAK.

ZACK'S PARENTS *REPORTED* HIM *MISSING* YESTERDAY, WHICH PUTS THE *CLOCK* AT ROUGHLY *FIFTY HOURS* SINCE HE WAS *LAST SEEN*.

ASSUMING HE'S *STILL* ALIVE, WE NEED TO *FIND* HIM.

ASSUMING HE *ISN'T*...

...WE NEED TO FIND THE *BODY*.

UNLESS MISTER *LIPPMAN* DECIDES HE WANTS TO *SAVE* US THE *TROUBLE*.

THIS IS ALL A *MISTAKE*.

NO, THE *MISTAKE* WAS *TRUSTING* YOU IN THE *FIRST* PLACE...

...BUT WE'RE **AIMING** TO **CORRECT** THAT ONE.

DAMMIT, **MAGGIE!** I **DIDN'T** SCREW YOU GUYS!

AND I **SURE** AS **HELL** HAVEN'T **KILLED** ANYONE!

IF THIS IS ABOUT THE **PHOTOGRAPH**--

OH, IT **IS**, SIMON, BUT I THINK WE'VE **FIGURED** THAT OUT.

WE ALL THOUGHT IT WAS A **CRIME SCENE** PHOTO THAT RAN OVER YOUR **BY-LINE** ON THE FRONT PAGE OF THE GAZETTE.

FIGURED YOU'D **BOUGHT** IT OFF OF **CORRIGAN**, THAT EITHER **HE** OR ONE OF HIS BUNKIES WAS YOUR **SOURCE**.

BUT THEY **WEREN'T**, WERE THEY? BECAUSE THE GAZETTE'S PHOTO **WASN'T** OUR PHOTO AT ALL...

...IT WAS A **DIFFERENT** ONE ALTOGETHER, TAKEN **BEFORE** WE EVEN ARRIVED...

...TAKEN BY **SOMEONE** WHO WAS ON THE **ROOF** AT THE **TIME** OF THE MURDER.

AND YOU THINK IT WAS **ME?**

I THINK IT'S A **HELL** OF A PHOTO TO **RUN** OVER YOUR **BY-LINE**, SIMON.

AND YOU'VE **ALWAYS** HAD A **NOSE** FOR A **GOOD** STORY.

SO **MAYBE** YOU DECIDED TO **MAKE** ONE ALL YOUR **OWN**.

I DON'T **KNOW** WHERE THE PHOTO CAME FROM!

TWO DAYS AGO YOU WERE GOING **ON** AND **ON** ABOUT HOW I COULDN'T **ASK** YOU TO GIVE UP A **SOURCE**.

WHICH STORY IS IT, SIMON?

BOTH. I *DIDN'T*--I *DON'T*--KNOW WHO TOOK THE PICTURE...

...AND YOU *DIDN'T* HAVE THE *RIGHT* TO ASK ME TO GIVE UP A *SOURCE!*

WHAT'S YOUR *CONNECTION* WITH SCOTT BENJAMIN, SIMON?

WHAT? WAIT, *THAT'S* THE *SECOND* VICTIM? *NONE!* WHY THE HELL WOULD YOU *EVEN* ASK ME *THAT?*

KID HAD ONE OF *YOUR* BUSINESS CARDS. WHY WOULD A SIXTEEN-YEAR-OLD HAVE ONE OF *YOUR* CARDS?

HALF THIS *DEPARTMENT* HAS MY *CARD,* CRIS!

IT *CONNECTS* YOU TO HIM.

I'M THINKING IT'S *JEALOUSY.*

MOLINA MADE *HAY* OUT OF THAT WHOLE *JOKER* CLUSTER-%$*#¢ LAST CHRISTMAS, MAYBE YOU WERE LOOKING TO MAKE SOME YOURSELF?

YOU DECIDED TO *MAKE* NEWS INSTEAD OF *COVERING* IT, GET A *BIG* STORY ALL YOUR *OWN.*

JINGLE HELL

C'MON, YOU GUYS *KNOW* ME.

YOU *KNOW* ME!

NO--

--WHAT I KNOW IS THAT A *THIRD* KID IS *MISSING!*

AND IF ZACK WESTON IS *DEAD* WHEN WE *FIND* HIM, I WILL *PAY* FOR THE PRIVILEGE OF FRYING YOU *MYSELF!*

COME *CLEAN,* SIMON. *HELP* YOUR-SELF.

WHERE'S THE *KID?*

HEY, UH... ROMY?

ON THE PHONE, STACY.

YEAH, BUT I'VE GOT--

EXCUSE ME?

YES?

WHO ARE THE DETECTIVES IN CHARGE OF THE DEAD ROBINS CASE?

THAT WOULD BE DETECTIVES DRIVER AND MACDONALD. I'M SORRY, AREN'T YOU PRESS?

YEAH, JUST FREELANCE, BUT...I NEED TO TALK TO DRIVER AND MACDONALD.

I'M AFRAID THAT'S NOT GOING TO BE POSSIBLE. YOU'RE NOT SUPPOSED TO BE UP HERE, EVEN.

HOW DID YOU GET PAST THE DESK SERGEANT?

JUST WALKED PAST HIM LIKE I KNEW WHAT I WAS DOING, NO ONE SAID A THING.

AMAZING... AND THEY WONDER ABOUT THE CRIME RATE...

WELL, LOOK, YOU'RE GONNA HAVE TO LEAVE, BECAUSE WE DON'T ALLOW--

I NEED TO SEE THEM ABOUT THIS.

HEADMONTE ACADEMY GOTHAM

Zack Weston

Zack Weston

JOSIE, CAN YOU AND MARCUS COME *HERE?*

JUST A SEC, STACY.

UH, MAYBE *NOW?*

STACY? WHAT'S GOING ON?

I UNDERSTAND YOU'VE TAKEN *SIMON LIPPMAN* INTO CUSTODY?

I'M SORRY. WHO ARE *YOU?*

STACE, WHO *IS* THIS?

HE'S GOT--

YOU'VE GOT THE WRONG MAN, DETECTIVE.

MOTHER$#%--

--YOU THE GOD'S HONEST *TRUTH* HERE, MAGGIE.

--IS THE *KID,* YOU SONNUVVABICH! WHERE *IS* HE?!

...WHAT THE *HELL?*

WHAT'D YOU DO WITH THE KID, YOU SICK--

DETECTIVES!

WHAT THE HELL IS GOING ON HERE?

SON OF A BITCH JUST WALKED IN WITH ZACK WESTON'S SCHOOL I.D. CARD.

WE'VE GOT THE WRONG GUY IN THE BOX, CAPTAIN.

WHAT?

IT'S THIS HUMP.

WHAT?

IS SIMON IN THERE? IN THE BOX?

YES, HE IS... WHO ARE YOU?

I'M NOBODY. JUST LIKE YOU.

BUT I'M A FRIEND OF SIMON'S. AND I'D LIKE TO TALK TO HIM.

GIVE HIM AN EXCLUSIVE FOR ALL HIS TROUBLE.

I DON'T LIKE THIS ONE BIT.

THAT'S WHY YOU'RE *SECOND SHIFT*, DETECTIVE.

I COULD *NOT* TELL.

HEY, I *GOT* THE GUY.

-- ANY CHANCE YOU COULD LEAVE US ALONE?

I'M *SURE* YOU'LL BE *RECORDING* THIS, ANYWAY.

'FRAID NOT, MR. DUNNING. CONSIDER US *BODYGUARDS*... WHAT YOU JUST PUT YOUR *FRIEND* HERE THROUGH, YOU MAY *NEED* ONE.

I'M SURE THAT'S NOT... TRUE?

SIMON?

WHAT THE HELL HAVE YOU *DONE*, DUNNING?

YOU'RE KILLING *CHILDREN?* HAVE YOU LOST YOUR $5#%ING MIND?

I...WELL...I CAN'T EXPECT YOU TO UNDERSTAND ALL OF IT, OF COURSE...BUT NO. I DON'T *THINK* I'VE LOST MY MIND.

THEN *WHY?*

IT'S KIND OF COMPLICATED--

WHY SET ME UP? WE WERE *FRIENDS*, JACK.

WE STILL ARE. I *CAME DOWN* AS SOON AS I *HEARD* THEY ARRESTED YOU.

I JUST WANTED TO BE SURE YOU'D BE HERE...FOR THE STORY.

SEE, I GOT THE IDEA WHEN I CAME ACROSS A GUY CALLED THE *TAILOR*, DOING BACKGROUND FOR A PIECE. HE COULD DUPLICATE ALMOST *ANY* COSTUME.

SO YOU GOT HIM TO MAKE YOU SOME ROBIN OUTFITS?

NO. HE HAD SOME FROM *BEFORE*. JOKER ORDERED A FEW HE NEVER PICKED UP OR SOMETHING.

ANYWAY, THAT'S ALL *SIDEBAR* STUFF, HUMAN INTEREST, MAYBE...THE POINT IS, IT GAVE ME AN *ENTRY POINT*, YOU KNOW?

ENTRY POINT TO *WHAT*?

THE WORLD.

YOU'RE *IN* THE WORLD, DUNNING.

NO...*THIS* ISN'T THE WORLD. NOT THE ONE YOU AND I LIVE IN, SIMON...THIS *ISN'T* THE *WORLD*.

LOOK, HOW ABOUT YOU TWO FINISH THIS ILLUMINATING LITTLE CHAT AFTER YOU TELL US WHERE *ZACK WESTON* IS... ASSUMING HE'S STILL *ALIVE*?

ZACK SHOULD BE *FINE* FOR ANOTHER FEW HOURS. BUT I CAN'T TELL *YOU* WHERE HE IS.

CAN YOU TELL *SIMON*, THEN?

NO, NOT *HIM*, EITHER... YOU STILL DON'T UNDERSTAND WHY I'M *HERE*, DO YOU? I CAN'T TELL ANYONE BUT THE BATMAN.

THIS IS MY ENTRY POINT. THIS IS HOW I ENTER *THEIR* WORLD.

C'MON, CAPTAIN, WE *KNOW* HOW THIS *ENDS*...

WAIT, MARCUS.

I JUST--

NO *GODDAMN* WAY!

LOWER YOUR *VOICE* AND *CLOSE* THE DOOR.

YOU *CANNOT* SERIOUSLY *CONSIDER* THIS, CAPTAIN!

TELL ME THIS IS *NOT* AN *OPTION*, HERE!

WHY THE HELL *NOT?*

WE *DO* THIS, WE *GIVE* DUNNING WHAT HE *WANTS*, MARCUS! WE END UP *VALIDATING* HIS *CRIME!*

THAT HAPPENS AND IT'LL BE *LET'S MAKE A DEAL* EVERY TIME WE RUN AN *INTERROGATION!*

WHICH WOULD *BOTHER* ME *MORE* IF THERE WASN'T A *KID'S* LIFE AT *STAKE*.

LET US *RUN* AT HIM AGAIN--

THERE *ISN'T* TIME, CRIS.

YOU *HEARD* DUNNING. HE'S GIVING ZACK WESTON A FEW HOURS TO *LIVE*, ON THE *OUTSIDE*.

COULD BE HE'S *BLUFFING*, CAPTAIN?

YOU *REALLY* WANT TO *TAKE* THAT *CHANCE?*

OKAY, SO HE **WANTS** BATMAN, LET'S **GIVE** HIM BATMAN.

I JUST **SAID**--

DOESN'T HAVE TO BE THE **REAL** DEAL, CRIS.

WHAT, YOU **FIGURE** I SHOULD JUST **SHOOT** OVER TO THIS **TAILOR'S** PLACE, GET MYSELF A **BATMAN** COSTUME?

DRESS UP AND TRY TO MAKE DUNNING **WET** HIMSELF?

YEAH, ON **SECOND** THOUGHT IT'S PROBABLY **NOT** SUCH A **GOOD** IDEA...

...ROMY MIGHT **TRY** TO **BUST A CAP** IN YOUR ASS.

YEAH, WELL, HE'D HAVE TO GIVE HER **WEAPON** BACK, FIRST.

WHAT WAS **THAT**?

OH, HELL.

NICE ONE, RENEE.

DID **I HEAR** THAT **RIGHT**? DID DETECTIVE CHANDLER TAKE A **SHOT** AT BATMAN?

DID BATMAN **TAKE** HER DUTY WEAPON?

IT'S **NOT** WHAT YOU **THINK**, CAPTAIN--

YOU HAVE **NO** IDEA **WHAT** I THINK, DETECTIVE DRIVER!

JESUS CHRIST, SHE'S A **POLICE**! SHE DOESN'T GO **SHOOTING** AT PEOPLE BECAUSE SHE DOESN'T **LIKE** THEM!

HE BROKE HER NOSE, **DIDN'T** HE?

I'M GOING TO HAVE TO **TALK** TO THE COMMISSIONER.

CAPTAIN...

KID'S GOT **HOURS**, CRIS. AT BEST.

MARCUS.

I'M **SORRY**, MAN, I DON'T KNOW **WHERE** MY HEAD --

FORGET ABOUT IT.

WE'RE **ALL** TIRED.

MICHAEL AKINS
Commissioner
of Police

YOU HAVE **GOT** TO BE **KIDDING** ME.

WE NEED TO PUT THE **SIGNAL** BACK UP, COMMISSIONER.

NO, SERIOUSLY, YOU HAVE **GOT** TO BE **KIDDING** ME, RIGHT?

THIS IS SOME **JOKE**, TRYING TO **LIGHTEN** THE MOOD BECAUSE OF ALL THE **CRAP** WE'VE BEEN GETTING FROM THE **PRESS**, RIGHT?

I THINK THERE'S A **SPARE** IN STORAGE.

TELL STACY TO MEET ME ON THE **ROOF**.

YES, SIR.

IT WOULD'VE BEEN A **GOOD** JOKE, THOUGH, YOU HAVE TO **ADMIT**.

YES, SIR.

I CAN **FIRE** YOU, YOU **KNOW** THAT, RIGHT, MAGGIE?

SO WHAT'S THIS, LIKE, THE **BACKUP** BAT-SIGNAL?

SOMETHING LIKE THAT. DEPARTMENT GOT IT AS A **GIFT** FROM KORD INDUSTRIES A FEW YEARS BACK, BUT WE HAD TO DECOMMISSION IT NOT LONG AFTER I GOT HERE.

CITY COUNCIL SAID IT WAS AN **INAPPROPRIATE** GIFT, SO WE WENT BACK TO THE OLD ONE.

POLITICS.

ABSOLUTELY.

PRETTY CONVENIENT THAT THIS ONE IS SO EASY TO SET UP.

YES. A LASER SIGNAL VISIBLE FOR 25 MILES IN ALL DIRECTIONS **IS** PREFERABLE TO PAINTING A BAT ON A FLASH-LIGHT, I SUPPOSE.

OKAY, THEN YOU JUST...

I THINK...OH, **THERE** IT IS.

THAT'S **IT**?

PRETTY MUCH.

I LIKE THE OTHER ONE BETTER.

WHAT DO **YOU** THINK, JOSIE? I--

JESUS!

THAT WAS QUICK. DID YOU ACTUALLY *WAIT* FOR THE SIGNAL, OR DO YOU HAVE *LISTENING DEVICES* IN MY OFFICE?

IS THERE A *REASON* YOU LIT THAT?

YOU THINK I'D *WASTE* MY RESOURCES ON YOU IF THERE WASN'T A *DAMN GOOD* REASON?

OKAY, ENOUGH. YOU TWO CAN FIGHT IT OUT LATER.

BUT RIGHT NOW, THERE'S A KID'S LIFE AT STAKE, REMEMBER? THAT'S WHY WE'RE HERE.

SIMON LIPPMAN ISN'T THE KILLER.

WE *KNOW* THAT. WE'VE GOT THE *REAL* PERP DOWNSTAIRS, AND THE THIRD VIC IS STILL BREATHING FOR NOW. BUT HE WON'T SAY *WHERE* HE IS...

YES, HE'LL ONLY GIVE *THAT* PIECE OF INFORMATION TO *YOU*.

KILL THE LIGHTS IN THE SQUAD ROOM... *AND* THE BOX.

89

...I SAW HIM; HE SPOKE TO ME...

SURE.

YOU'RE BLOCKING MY OFFICE, SIMON.

I KNOW.

IF YOU'RE LOOKING FOR AN APOLOGY...

I KNOW YOU BETTER THAN THAT, EVEN IF YOU DON'T KNOW ME.

I WILL TAKE A COMMENT, HOWEVER. SOMETHING ABOUT BATMAN'S INVOLVEMENT.

ON THE RECORD.

AKINS WILL KILL ME.

THEN WE'LL BE ABOUT SQUARE.

"HIS HELP WAS INSTRUMENTAL IN THE ARREST," M.C.U. CAPTAIN SAWYER SAID.

"AS WAS THE ASSISTANCE OF CERTAIN JOURNALISTS FROM THE LOCAL MEDIA."

HOW'S THAT?

PROBABLY WON'T USE THE LAST PART.

GET SOME SLEEP, MAGGIE.

YOU LOOK BEAT.

--CORRECT, ZACK WESTON WAS RETURNED TO HIS FAMILY SAFELY. HE WAS BEING HELD IN A SUBBASEMENT IN THE EAST END.

COMMISSIONER, WE UNDERSTAND THAT SIMON LIPPMAN FROM THE GAZETTE WAS TAKEN INTO CUSTODY EARLIER. WAS MR. LIPPMAN A SUSPECT?

Commissioner Michael Akins

LIVE

ROBIN KILLER CAPTURED
THIRD BOY SAVED 10

NO, MR. LIPPMAN WAS A SUBJECT, NOT A SUSPECT. AND AS I'M SURE YOU'LL READ, HE WAS INSTRUMENTAL IN AIDING THE G.C.P.D. IN THIS INVESTIGATION...

LOOK AT THAT MAN...DEFLECTS THE QUESTION LIKE A CONSUMMATE POLITICIAN AND COVERS OUR ASSES AT THE SAME TIME.

HE REALLY SHOULD RUN FOR MAYOR.

HE PROBABLY WILL, SARGE.

--SAY TO REPORTS OF THE BAT-SIGNAL BEING SIGHTED EARLIER TONIGHT, COMMISSIONER?

NO COMMENT?

NO COMMENT.

NO COMMENT. NEXT?

--IS DETECTIVE CHANDLER?

HAVE NOT SEEN HER, CAP. TRY THE BREAK ROOM YET?

DETECTIVE ROMY CHANDLER. JUST THE WOMAN I WAS LOOKING FOR.

OH, UH... WHAT'S UP, CAPTAIN?

I BETTER GET BACK TO MY DESK...

AM I TO UNDERSTAND THAT *IN ADDITION* TO YOUR APPARENT *SHOOTING* OF BATMAN...

...THAT YOU *ALSO* LOST YOUR SERVICE WEAPON?

...THAT'S NOT...

SORRY TO *INTERRUPT*, CAPTAIN, BUT I THINK THERE'S BEEN A *MISUNDERSTANDING*.

I JUST *PICKED UP* ROMY'S PIECE FROM REPAIR. HER SIGHTS WERE *WAY OFF*.

YEAH... THAT'S WHY MY *WARNING SHOT* ACCIDENTALLY HIT.

IS THAT THE STORY YOU'RE STICKING WITH?

IF YOU'LL BUY IT.

NEVER HAPPEN AGAIN, CAPTAIN. SCOUT'S HONOR.

SEE THAT IT DOESN'T. YOU'RE A GOOD DETECTIVE, ROMY. WE'D HATE TO LOSE YOU.

STACY GOT IT FROM ROBIN.

I KNOW.

DAMN.

WHAT *IS* IT WITH THIS CITY...?

IT'S A LOVE/HATE THING, ROMY...

THERE'S A LOT HERE TO LOVE...THAT YOU WON'T FIND IN ANY OTHER CITY IN THE WORLD...

...BUT THERE'S JUST AS MUCH THAT'LL KILL YOU, EITHER IN AN INSTANT OR SLOWLY...DAY BY DAY...

Gotham Gazette

ROBIN KILLER CONFESSES

Croc Escapes

BUT WHAT ARE YOU GONNA DO? *QUIT? LEAVE?*

NO...THIS IS MY *CITY.*

I COULD SOONER LEAVE *YOU.*

HEY!

AND THAT'S *NOT* GOING TO HAPPEN, MARCUS...

LET'S GO HOME.

SUNDAY BLOODY SUNDAY

The cosmic cataclysm known as the Infinite Crisis is wreaking havoc all across the Galaxy. As an all-too-powerful madman is molding the laws of nature and physics like clay, the properties of magic are also changing, and all of the wielders of magic are losing control of their powers. The most powerful of all the supernatural guardians is the Spectre — the living spirit of vengeance. The Spectre relies on a human host for moral guidance, but has been without one for too long. Whoever he chooses as his next host will become the arbiter of morality for all humankind.

THEY SAY THE **WORLD** IS COMING TO AN **END.**

WOULDN'T BE THE **FIRST** TIME.

FACT IS, IT HAPPENS MORE OFTEN THAN MOST PEOPLE CARE TO **ADMIT.**

HELL, **SOME** SCIENTISTS CLAIM THE EARTH HAS HAD ITS TICKET **PUNCHED** A HALF-DOZEN TIMES IN THE LAST FOUR **BILLION** YEARS.

GOTHAM GAL KILLER BODY!

AND THAT'S **NOT** COUNTING WHAT HAPPENED TO THE **DINOSAURS.**

CURRENT THINKING IN **PHYSICS** IS THAT **UNIVERSES**--PLURAL-- ARE **BEGINNING** AND **ENDING** ALL THE TIME.

THAT **OURS** IS JUST A **BLIP** IN THE **COSMIC** SCHEME, THAT'S **ALL.**

EXTINCTION **HAPPENS** ON SOME SCALE **EVERY** MOMENT. MURDER OR EVOLUTION OR DIVINE ACT, **PICK** YOUR **POISON.**

SOME MORE **NATURAL** THAN **OTHERS.**

THERE'S AN **OLD** MURDER POLICE JOKE.

WELL?

HOMICIDE. WE WORK FOR **GOD.**

IT'S **DEAD.**

I DON'T THINK ABOUT GOD THAT MUCH ANYMORE.

AFTER YOU'VE SEEN A *GOOD* COP FROZEN *SOLID* BY MISTER *FREEZE* AND THEN *SHATTERED* LIKE A PORCELAIN *DOLL*, YOUR *FAITH* TAKES A *BEATING*.

...DISPATCH AND A *TOW TRUCK*, AND SOONER RATHER THAN LATER, OKAY?

TEN-FOUR.

SEE ENOUGH ACTS LIKE *THAT*, IT'S *EASIER* NOT TO THINK ABOUT GOD'S *MERCY* AND HIS *DIVINE WILL* TOO MUCH.

GONNA BE *HALF* AN HOUR, AT THE *LEAST*.

BUSY NIGHT?

OR ELSE YOU FIND YOURSELF ASKING *QUESTIONS* THAT HAVE *NO* ANSWER.

THAT'S THE *THING*. THERE'S *NOTHING* HAPPENING, THE WHOLE DAMN *CITY* IS DEAD.

FIND YOURSELF WONDERING *WHY*.

HOLDING ITS *BREATH*.

YOU GET THE *FEELING* IT'S GOING TO BE *ONE* OF *THOSE* NIGHTS?

SO I *TRY* NOT TO *THINK* ABOUT IT TOO MUCH. IT'S LIKE THAT LINE IN THE PLAY, *MEDEA*.

HELL YEAH.

"WE MUSTN'T *THINK* TOO MUCH. PEOPLE GO *MAD* IF THEY *THINK* TOO MUCH."

MY WIFE, DORE, SHE DOESN'T **UNDERSTAND** WHY I WON'T GO TO CHURCH ANYMORE.

...NO, THE **UNMARKED** BROKE DOWN, SO RENEE AND I ARE OUT OF THE SQUAD ROOM UNTIL WE CAN GET A **LIFT** BACK...

...I WILL...YES, I'LL TELL HER...KISS THE **BOYS** FOR ME...

YOU, TOO BABY

IT'S ONE OF THE **FEW** THINGS WE ACTUALLY **FIGHT** ABOUT. SHE THINKS IT GIVES OUR **SONS** THE **WRONG** IMPRESSION.

"BABY"?

WHAT, YOU DON'T HAVE A TERM OF **ENDEARMENT** FOR DARIA?

WHAT I CALL DARIA IS **NONE** OF YOUR **DAMN** BUSINESS.

I'VE TRIED TELLING HER THAT **RIGHT** AND **WRONG** DON'T HAVE TO **ONLY** BE TAUGHT IN A **CHURCH.**

SO I DID SOME **DIGGING** ON THE **CORRIGAN** THING --

SHE TELLS ME THAT'S **NOT** THE POINT.

DAMMIT, CRIS, **NOT** AGAIN --

YES, **AGAIN.** THERE'S A **STORY** GOING AROUND, RENEE, ABOUT YOU AND CORRIGAN AT FINNIGAN'S BAR...

IT **ENDS** THERE, BECAUSE THE ONLY THING I CAN **SAY** TO HER MY WIFE DOESN'T **WANT** TO HEAR.

...THAT YOU **TOOK** HIM OUT BACK AND **BEAT** THE LIVING **HELL** OUT OF HIM.

I DON'T BELIEVE IN GOD ANYMORE.

IS THAT HOW YOU GOT THE **MISSING** BULLET, THE **ONE** THAT **CLEARED** ME?

CRIS --

I WANT AN **ANSWER,** PARTNER.

YOU **OWE** ME AN **ANSWER.**

RENEE MONTOYA'S BEEN MY **PARTNER** FOR **YEARS** NOW.

CORRIGAN **SOLD** IT, I HAD TO FIND OUT WHO **TO**, AND HE **WASN'T** TALKING.

I **DID** WHAT I **HAD** TO, CRIS.

IN MANY WAYS, SHE KNOWS ME **BETTER** THAN MY OWN **WIFE.**

GOD **DAMMIT,** RENEE! WHAT THE HELL WERE YOU **THINKING?**

WE'RE **NOT** GOING TO **HAVE** THIS --

IN MANY WAYS, I **KNOW** HER BETTER THAN HER LOVER, DARIA.

I DON'T KNOW IF DARIA'S **SEEN** IT.

NO, WE **ARE** GOING TO HAVE THIS CONVERSATION!

GET **OFF** OF ME!

I **KNOW** FOR A **FACT** THAT CAPTAIN SAWYER **HASN'T.**

ARE YOU **OUT** OF YOUR **MIND,** RENEE?

BY **BEATING** CORRIGAN DOWN, YOU **KILLED** ANY CHANCE OF **US** OR I.A.D. **EVER** MAKING A **CASE** AGAINST THAT **ROTTEN** SON OF A BITCH.

BUT **I** HAVE.

YOU **PLAYED** HIS **GAME,** YOU **SUNK** TO HIS **LEVEL.** AND **NOW** WE'RE **STUCK** WITH HIM IN THE **C.S.U.,** PARTNER.

WHAT THE **HELL** WERE YOU **THINKING?**

SHE'S IN **TROUBLE.**

I WAS THINKING THAT **PROTECTING** YOU WAS MORE IMPORTANT THAN **NAILING** HIM, CRIS.

THAT'S WHAT I WAS THINKING.

≤SKSHHS≤-- ANY **AVAILABLE** UNIT!

IT **STARTED** AFTER THE THING WITH **TWO-FACE.**

TEN-THREE! TEN-THREE, CATHEDRAL SQUARE!

MULTIPLE FREAKS, WE'VE GOT --

SHE'S BEEN GETTING **MORE** AND **MORE** RECKLESS EVER **SINCE.**

KRAK KRAK KRAK KRAK

EEEEEE

GOD OH MY GOD IT'S RIDDLER IT'S--

ANGRIER AND ANGRIER.

DAMMIT DAMMIT DAMMIT DAMMIT!

EEEEEEEEEE

WHERE SHE **USED** TO **HATE** THE **VIOLENCE** OF THE JOB...

PULL OVER!

PULL IT OVER!

...**NOW** SHE ALMOST **RUNS** INTO ITS **EMBRACE.**

M.C.U.! WE'RE TAKING YOUR **RIDE!**

THE HELL?

GOTHAM

AND I'M **SCARED** FOR HER.

OUT OF THE **WAY,** BARBIE!

HEY!

SCARED FOR WHERE IT MAY **LEAD** HER.

WE'LL HAVE **DISPATCH** SEND A **PICKUP** FOR YOU!

THERE'S *RELIEF* IN BEING ON THE *MOVE* AGAIN, AT LEAST.

ALL UNITS, RESPOND CATHEDRAL SQUARE, TEN-THIRTY-THREE.

CHARLIE TANGO FOUR, MOBILE, RESPONDING...

NO ONE WANTS TO BE *SITTING* ON THEIR *HANDS* WHEN THE *APOCALYPSE* COMES, AFTER ALL.

...BE ADVISED CHARLIE TANGO FOUR NOW THREE-TWO BAKER.

BETTER TO AT LEAST *FEEL* LIKE WE'RE DOING SOMETHING.

ALL UNITS, SUSPECTS *IDENTIFIED* AS THE RIDDLER, THE SCAVENGER, MURMUR, THE BODY DOUBLES, RED PANZER AND THE FISHERMAN...

WE'RE NOT *DONE*, BY THE *WAY*.

THE *IRONY* THAT WE'RE HEADING TO *CATHEDRAL SQUARE* HASN'T *ESCAPED* ME, EITHER.

...OTHERS MAY BE *PRESENT*, PROCEED WITH *CAUTION*. E.S.U. IS RESPONDING.

THIS THING WITH *CORRIGAN* IS --

WOULD YOU *SHUT UP* ABOUT *CORRIGAN*, ALREADY?

YES, HE'S *CORRUPT* AND YES, HE'S *STILL* ON THE *FORCE*, BUT THEN AGAIN SO ARE *YOU*!

AND THAT'S A *FAIR TRADE* IN MY ...

THE *EDGE* IN HER *VOICE* VANISHES.

...BOOK UH... CRIS...?

I RAISE MY *EYES*...

THE SKY BEGINS TO RAIN FIRE.

AH!

MOTHER%*$#!

METAL *TEARS* AS SOMETHING *CRUSHES* THE ENGINE BLOCK.

THE WINDSHIELD *EXPLODES* INWARDS, SHOWERING ME WITH *SAFETY* GLASS.

I TUMBLE OUT OF THE *CAR* AND INTO *AIR* THAT *STINKS* OF *SULFUR* AND BURNING *FLESH.*

MY SIGHT *CATCHES* ON ONE *WORD* AND A *FACE...*

...AND I *FREEZE* FOR A MOMENT, STARING INTO THE *EYES* OF A *SIN.*

SCREAMS AND EXPLOSIONS ECHO THROUGHOUT THE SQUARE.

RENEE'S SAYING SOMETHING, BUT I CAN'T *HEAR* HER.

OF ALL THE THINGS THAT SHOULD BE *FRIGHTENING* ME AT *THIS* MOMENT AND *AREN'T*...

IS THAT...?

CAPTAIN MARVEL.

...THIS ONE *DOES*.

AND THEN HE *SPEAKS*, AND I DON'T *UNDERSTAND* WHAT HE'S SAYING.

THE ROCK OF ETERNITY... THE *ROCK*...HE... DID IT...

...THE SPECTRE...

...HE *KILLED* HIM...

AND NOW I AM *TRULY* AFRAID.

...HE KILLED THE WIZARD...

THE THINGS I'VE SEEN, SO MANY THINGS...

WHAT... WHAT IS THAT...?

...BATMAN IN THE NIGHT SKY AND THE JOKER IN THE BOX AND MURDER A THOUSAND TIMES OVER...

...BUT NOTHING LIKE THIS, NOTHING EVER LIKE THIS...

THE SPECTRE, THE AGENT OF DIVINE VENGEANCE.

BUT HE'S GONE MAD, HE'S UNRAVELING ALL MAGICK--

HNH!

RENEE MAKES A NOISE, IT'S THE SOUND I IMAGINE A SHARK WOULD MAKE WHEN IT SMELLS BLOOD IN THE WATER--

PARTNER?

BASTARDS BASTARDS--

--AND SUDDENLY IT'S AS IF ALL THAT ANGER SHE'S BEEN CARRYING CAN NO LONGER BE CONTAINED.

--BASTARDS DO THIS TO ME TO THEIR CHILD THEY THINK I DON'T KNOW--

RENEE!

--WHAT THEY THINK THEY'RE SAYING BEHIND MY BACK WHAT ALL OF YOU THINK YOU SAY YOU BASTARDS--

I'VE GOT JUST LONG ENOUGH TO SEE THE IRONY IN BEING KILLED BY MY BEST FRIEND...

--I'LL KILL YOU, I'LL £*%#1NG SON OF A--

...AND THEN CAPTAIN MARVEL MAYBE SAVES **BOTH** OUR LIVES, JUST LIKE THAT.

--**HANDS** OFF OF ME YOU **NAIVE** DO-GOODING--

LEAVE HER ALONE.

NOW.

SOMETHING... **LEAVES** HER BODY...

UNNH!

...THE **FURY** OF THE **DEVIL** HIMSELF.

THEN CAPTAIN MARVEL IS **TALKING** TO ME LIKE I **UNDERSTAND** WHAT'S GOING ON.

CAN YOU TAKE **CARE** OF HER?

THE **POSSESSION** WAS ONLY **TEMPORARY,** BUT SHE'LL NEED A FEW **MINUTES** TO REGAIN HER **STRENGTH.**

POSSESSION?

WITH THE ROCK OF ETERNITY **SHATTERED,** THE **SEVEN DEADLY SINS** ARE **FREE** UPON GOTHAM, OFFICER.

AND I CANNOT **STAY** TO HELP **FIGHT** THEM.

BUT YOU'RE--

THE WIZARD IS DEAD, I DON'T EXPECT YOU TO UNDERSTAND.

BUT MY FAMILY...MY FAMILY MAY BE IN GREAT DANGER, I MUST GO TO THEM.

MY STOMACH SHRINKS, THE FEAR RACING UP MY SPINE.

I'M SORRY.

IF HE'S WORRIED ABOUT HIS FAMILY SURVIVING THIS NIGHT...

...THEN WHAT HOPE DOES MINE HAVE?

I'VE GOT TO GET TO THEM.

CRIS?

EASY, PARTNER.

I'VE GOT TO GET TO THEM NOW.

I'M SORRY, I'M SO SORRY, I DIDN'T—I DIDN'T MEAN IT...

WHAT I SAID...I DIDN'T MEAN...

DON'T WORRY ABOUT IT RIGHT NOW...

...WE'VE GOT TO GET MOVING.

I'VE GOT TWO **HUNDRED** BLOCKS TO **COVER** FROM HERE TO **HOME.**

TWO HUNDRED **BLOCKS** THROUGH A GOTHAM THAT HAS ONCE **AGAIN** GONE **MAD.**

TWO HUNDRED **BLOCKS** WITH MY **PARTNER** ON MY ARM AND SEVEN DEADLY SINS HAVING A **FIELD** DAY...

...JUST TAKE IT **ONE** STEP AT A **TIME,** CRIS...

THE **WIND** THAT'S BEEN **HOWLING** FOR THE LAST THREE MINUTES WHIPS **TEAR GAS** INTO MY **FACE.**

≥KAFF≤

≥KOFF≤

JUST THE **BAREST** TOUCH AND IT'S **ENOUGH** TO START THE **WATERWORKS** FLOWING.

THAT'S THE **LEAST** OF OUR **PROBLEMS.**

I **RECOGNIZE** HIM FROM SOME **PERP BOOK** OF **FREAKS** FROM YEARS AGO...

...THE **FISHERMAN,** I THINK HE'S **CALLED,** ONE OF **AQUAMAN'S** ROGUES...

DROP BAIT.

...AND IN **ANY** OTHER CIRCUMSTANCE, I'D BE **LAUGHING** AT THE **SIGHT** OF **HIM.**

I GO FOR MY **GUN.**

HE'S FASTER.

WHY ARE THEY **ALWAYS** FASTER?

NYAA

THE **GUN** KICKS IN MY **HAND.**

I **MISS.**

THIS ISN'T **CATCH** AND **RELEASE.**

I DON'T GET A **SECOND** SHOT.

HNHH

PAIN SPIRALS UP MY **ARM.**

ANOTHER ⸨*⸩%ING **COP,** HUH?

BETWEEN THE *TEAR GAS* AND HIS *GRIP*, MY *LUNGS* HAVE *NOTHING*.

I £%(*ING HATE *COPS*.

THE *EDGES* OF THE *WORLD* TURN TO *WHITE*. I HEAR THE *ROAR* OF THE *OCEAN* IN MY *EARS*.

I'M BEING *SUFFOCATED* BY A *LUNATIC* CALLED THE *FISHERMAN*.

KRAK

I THINK OF MY *FAMILY*, AND THAT THIS IS A *STUPID GODDAMN* WAY TO *LEAVE* THEM.

HUH?

KRAKKRAKKRAK

WHAZZIT?

IT TAKES A *SECOND* FOR ME TO *RECOGNIZE* DETECTIVES MARCUS DRIVER AND JOSIE MACDONALD.

IT TAKES *ANOTHER* BEFORE I CAN SPEAK.

RENEE... RENEE'S BEEN *HURT.*

CRIS? YOU *OKAY?*

DOESN'T LOOK *TOO* BAD.

'M FINE.

WE GOT TO GET HER *OFF* THE *STREET,* MARCUS.

HERE, HOLD *STILL.*

LISTEN, MARCUS, CAN YOU AND *JO* TAKE CARE OF HER, GET HER *HOME?*

ARE YOU *KIDDING* ME? HAVE YOU *LOOKED* AROUND YOU, CRIS?

WORLD IS COMING TO AN *END,* IT'S *HATS* AND *BATS* TIME FOR THE G.C.P.D., ALL *COPS* ON THE *STREET.*

I'VE GOT TO GET TO MY *FAMILY,* MAN. AND RENEE NEEDS *HELP.*

THIS'LL *HURT.*

SONOFABITCH

YOU'RE GONNA NEED THIS *STITCHED* UP.

I'VE GOT TO GET TO MY *FAMILY.* CAN YOU AT *LEAST* GET RENEE TO AN *AMBO?*

THERE *ARE* NO AMBULANCES, CRIS. THERE'S *NOTHING...*

...I'M SORRY, MAN, BUT YOU GUYS ARE *ON* YOUR *OWN...*

I TRY **NOT TO BLAME** HIM, BECAUSE I KNOW HE'S RIGHT.

I SHOULD BE STANDING **BESIDE** THEM, HOLDING THE **LINE.**

BUT I'M **NOT,** AND I **DO** BLAME HIM.

NO CROSSING

DRIVER, JOSIE...THEY **DON'T** HAVE **FAMILIES** WAITING FOR THEM.

I TRY MY **PHONE,** DESPERATE TO HEAR DORE'S VOICE, OR THE **BOYS...**

--CIRCUITS ARE **BUSY,** PLEASE TRY YOUR CALL **AGAIN...**

IT TELLS ME WHAT I **EXPECTED,** BUT **NOT** WHAT I'D **HOPED.**

WITH **ALL** THE **LOOTING** GOING ON, I DON'T **SEE** THEM UNTIL THEY'RE IN FRONT OF US.

WHERE YOU GOING, **BOY?**

GOTHAM IS **BURNING,** BUT IT SEEMS THERE'S **ALWAYS** TIME FOR A LITTLE OLD-FASHIONED **RACISM.**

YOUR **GIRLFRIEND** DOESN'T **LOOK** SO GOOD, SPOOKY.

WHY DON'T YOU **LEAVE** HER WITH **US?** WE'LL TAKE **CARE** OF HER.

I THINK ABOUT WHAT **MARVEL** SAID, ABOUT SEVEN DEADLY SINS LET LOOSE IN THE **WORLD...**

...AND I WONDER HOW **MUCH** OF THIS IS **THEIR** DOING...

WALK AWAY. NOW.

LOOK AT **THAT,** THE **MONKEY'S** GOT A BADGE...

THAT'S RIGHT, HE'S A **COP...**

...AND HOW **MUCH** IS ALL OURS.

...WHICH MEANS HE'S GOT A **GUN...**

F&*%@&.

I POUND ON THE DOOR HOPING THAT EVERYONE HASN'T GONE HOME.

DARIA! DARIA HERNANDEZ!

IT'S DETECTIVE ALLEN!

THEY HAVEN'T.

RENEE!

IT'S THE FIRST PIECE OF LUCK WE'VE CAUGHT THE WHOLE NIGHT.

WHAT HAPPENED?

HEY, BABY, WHAT'S THE SPECIAL?

THE CITY'S GONE MAD, THAT'S WHAT'S HAPPENED, DEE!

ARE YOU GOOD HERE?

WE'VE GOT FOOD FOR AT LEAST A WEEK AND WINE FOR AT LEAST A MONTH.

AND LEO THERE IS DAMN QUICK WITH HIS EIGHT-INCH HOLLOW EDGE KERSHAW.

GOOD, OKAY, THEN I'M GOING TO LEAVE YOU GUYS HERE, ALL RIGHT?

YOU'RE HEADED HOME?

YEAH.

THANK YOU. FOR TAKING CARE OF HER.

SHE'S MY PARTNER, DEE.

SHE HAS NO IDEA HOW LUCKY SHE IS TO HAVE YOU.

OR TO HAVE YOU.

TAKE MY CAR, IT'S IN THE LOT AROUND BACK.

GIVE DORE AND THE BOYS MY LOVE.

BY THE TIME I'VE GONE *FOUR BLOCKS,* I'VE *ALREADY* COUNTED *SEVENTY-NINE* FELONIES.

I THINK ABOUT *STOPPING,* ABOUT DOING MY *JOB.*

THEN I THINK THAT I HAVE *NO* WEAPON, *NO* RADIO, AND *NO* HOPE OF *BACKUP.*

I *DRIVE,* AND SEE *EVERY* ONE OF THE *DEADLY SINS* HAVING ITS *DAY.*

I FOCUS ON THE *ROAD,* AND *NOT* WHAT'S *AROUND* ME.

NORTH OF NINETY-SECOND, GOTHAM TURNS TO A *GHOST TOWN.*

I TAKE IT UP TO *NINETY* AND *RUN* EVERY LIGHT.

I'M *STILL* NOT GOING *FAST* ENOUGH.

I JUST WANT TO GET HOME.

Equal Rights Are Not Special Rights

I JUST WANT TO GET HOME...

...*DOZENS* KILLED, THE *MAYOR* IS APPEALING TO THE *GOVERNOR* FOR *HELP...*

DAD! I GOT HOME AS **SOON** AS I COULD.

OH, **CRIS...**

...I WAS **PRAYING** YOU WERE ALL RIGHT.

CRISPUS, YOUR **ARM.**

IT'S **NOTHING,** DON'T **WORRY--**

WHAT'S GOING ON, DAD? WHAT'S **HAPPENING?**

I DON'T **KNOW,** JAKE. **CRAZY** THINGS.

THE GUY ON THE **TV** SAID THE **WORLD** WAS ENDING...

...HE SAID IT WAS THE **END** OF THE **WORLD.** WHAT ARE WE **SUPPOSED** TO DO?

WHAT ARE WE SUPPOSED TO **DO,** DAD?

WE **DON'T** LOSE **FAITH,** JACOB.

UNDER-STAND ME?

WE GIVE **THANKS** THAT WE'RE **ALL** TOGETHER AGAIN.

WE **THANK** GOD FOR OUR **FAMILY.**

AND WE **PRAY.**

GOTHAM CENTRAL

CORRIGAN 2

In a Police Department with a well-earned reputation as being one of the most corrupt, Crime Scene Technician Jim Corrigan has mastered the art of payoffs, extortion and exploitation. While investigating Corrigan, Inspector Manuel "Manny" Esperanza of the Internal Affairs Division learned of a scheme to frame M.C.U. Detective Crispus Allen. Manny informed Allen's partner Renee Montoya of the plot. Montoya used excessive force to get the information she needed from Corrigan, which cleared Allen, but her actions spared Corrigan from further investigation into his illicit affairs. He is essentially untouchable. Allen knew nothing of Renee's actions or their repercussions, until now.

12-7
23:20 Corriganto
Finnegan's
12-8
00:56 Leaves Finn's
01:14 Frank's Diner
(again)→meets
Bill Kenzie
02:01 Kenzie departs
– argument?

120

LATE NIGHT?

THIS FROM THE GUY WHO LOOKS LIKE HE GOT MAYBE AN *HOUR'S* SLEEP?

THAT'S AN HOUR MORE THAN *YOU*, FROM THE LOOKS OF IT, AND AT LEAST I MANAGED A *CHANGE* OF CLOTHES.

DORE SAYS THAT *DARIA* CALLED *AGAIN* LAST NIGHT, LOOKING FOR YOU.

DORE SAYS? *NOT* YOU?

I WAS *OUT*.

YOU WERE OUT AT *MIDNIGHT*?

SO WERE *YOU*, APPARENTLY...

...DIFFERENCE IS, I'M NOT MAKING A REGULAR *THING* OF IT, AND DORE *KNEW* I WAS GOING TO BE *LATE*.

SO NOW I'M WONDERING WHY *YOUR* GIRLFRIEND IS CALLING *MY* WIFE AT *MIDNIGHT* LOOKING FOR YOU.

AND *I'M* WONDERING WHY *YOU* WEREN'T AT *HOME* TO TAKE THAT CALL, BUT YOU *DON'T* HEAR *ME* ASKING, DO YOU?

ALL RIGHT, COME HERE.

CRIS, GET YOUR *HAND*--

COME. HERE.

...PUBLICIST CLAIMS HE IS **NOT** THE **FATHER**...

OOOH, I SMELL A **PATERNITY** SUIT.

SHUT UP, TOMMY.

...CLAIMING HE IS STILL HAPPILY MARRIED TO THE STAR OF **FALLING DOWN** IS FUNNY, IONA SHAUGHNESSY...

CURIOUSER AND CURIOUSER.

DON'T EVEN **THINK** ABOUT IT.

CRIS, I'VE GOT **WORK** TO--

SHUT **UP** AND LISTEN.

HEY, DON'T **TALK** TO ME LIKE **THAT**!

OR **WHAT**, YOU'RE GONNA **HIT** ME? THAT'S YOUR **NEW** THING, **RIGHT**?

A LITTLE **VIOLENCE** TO **EASE** YOUR **PAIN**, WHATEVER IT IS?

YOU ARE **SO** OFF-BASE HERE, **PARTNER**--

AM I?

YOU **MISSED** A SPOT.

PARTNER.

CHRIST.

YOU'RE COMING **APART**, RENEE.

AND I DON'T WANT TO **WATCH** IT ANYMORE.

I'M **FINE**.

...POCKET TEST ON IT, BUT IT SURE AS HELL *LOOKS* PURE...

...ANYONE SEEN KENZIE?

...DOWN TO THE WESTERN FOR *QUESTIONING*...

LONG.

HEY, CORRIGAN. YOU GOT HERE *FAST*.

YOU KNOW ME, *WHEREVER* THERE'S CRIME...

...I'LL BE *THERE*. YOU *DROPPED* THIS AT *FINNIGAN'S* LAST NIGHT.

YOU'D *THINK* I'D BE *MORE* CAREFUL WITH MY *MONEY*.

THANKS FOR *HOLDING* THIS FOR ME, JIMMY.

YEAH, WELL, THANKS FOR THE *TIP*.

KENZIE IN THERE?

IN THE *BEDROOM*, THAT'S WHERE THE *MAJOR* OPERATION WAS.

RIGHT. GIVE MULCAHEY MY *BEST*, WOULD YOU?

SURE THING.

124

HEY, CORRIGAN.

HEY, MATT.

WHAT ARE YOU *DOING* HERE, CORRIGAN?

HEARD *NARCOTICS* PULLED A *MAJOR* BUST, THOUGHT YOU GUYS MIGHT NEED A LITTLE *C.S.U.* HELP.

WHAT IS THIS, ABOUT *THIRTY* KEYS?

CLOSER TO *FORTY,* ALL PURE. HASN'T EVEN BEEN *CUT* FOR *STREET* SALE YET.

AND YOU COULD AT LEAST *TRY* TO BE *SUBTLE,* HERE.

NOT *EVERY* COP IS ON YOUR *PAYROLL,* Y'KNOW?

JUST WANTED TO COME AND *STAKE* MY *CLAIM,* BILLY.

SO *WHAT* CAN YOU *DO* FOR ME?

I'M HOLDING BACK *FIVE* KEYS ON THE *INVENTORY.*

DOUBLE IT, I'LL TAKE IT *ALL.* YOU *KNOW* WHERE TO BRING IT.

SEE YOU *TONIGHT.*

CRIS.

HMM?

CRIS.

I'M *SORRY,* OKAY?

YEAH, THERE'S *SINCERITY* JUST *DRIPPING* FROM THAT *APOLOGY.*

CUT ME A *LITTLE* SLACK, WE'RE IN THE *MIDDLE* OF THE *GODDAMN* SQUADROOM!

THAT'S A *GOOD* EXCUSE. TELL ME *ANOTHER.*

WHAT DO YOU WANT ME TO *SAY?* I'M *SORRY,* ALL RIGHT?

IT'S *NOT* WHAT I WANT YOU TO *SAY,* RENEE, IT'S WHAT I WANT YOU TO *DO.*

GET SOME *HELP,* SOMETHING, BEFORE YOU DO SOMETHING YOU'RE *REALLY* GOING TO *REGRET.*

I'M *FINE,* I'M JUST IN A *ROUGH* PATCH, THAT'S ALL.

BLEET BLEET

SURE.

AND *I'M* THE SCARECROW.

BLEET

BLEET

M.C.U., ALLEN...

...I CAN DO IT *NOW,* JUST TELL ME *WHERE...*

...NO, *NOT* THERE...

...THAT'LL *WORK.* GIVE ME *TWENTY* MINUTES.

I'VE GOT TO GO OUT.

WHO WAS THAT?

I'LL BE BACK IN AN HOUR OR SO.

I'LL COME WITH YOU.

NO.

I'M YOUR PARTNER--

IT'S ONE OF MY C.I.'S, HE GETS TWITCHY IF ANYONE SHOWS UP BESIDES ME, OKAY?

I KNOW ALL YOUR CONFIDENTIAL INFORMANTS, CRIS.

THIS ONE'S NEW, I HAVEN'T REGISTERED HIM YET.

I'LL BE BACK IN AN HOUR.

CORRIGAN.

...THEN *DOWN* FOR THE *HEARING* AT *TWO*.

INTERNAL AFFAIRS DIVISION

I'LL CALL AND LET THEM KNOW.

THANKS, *LIZ*.

ESPERANZA!

DETECTIVE MONTOYA, WHAT BRINGS YOU TO I.A.D.?

EXPLAIN THIS!

WHERE'D YOU *GET* IT?

YOU KNOW *DAMN WELL* WHERE I *GOT* IT!

NO, THAT'S WHY I'M *ASKING*.

BUT IF YOU WANT TO ACCUSE ME OF *ANYTHING*, PLEASE, FEEL FREE TO JOIN ME IN MY *OFFICE*.

M. ESPERANZA
INSPECTOR

YOU'VE GOT MY *PARTNER* WORKING ON *CORRIGAN!*

I DON'T HAVE *ANYONE* WORKING ON *CORRIGAN*, DETECTIVE MONTOYA, AND I THINK YOU *KNOW* WHY.

OR HAVE YOU *FORGOTTEN* THE LITTLE *TWO-STEP* YOU AND HE *DANCED* OUTSIDE OF *FINNIGAN'S* LAST FALL?

WAIT...

...ARE YOU *SAYING* THAT DETECTIVE ALLEN IS *INVESTIGATING* JAMES CORRIGAN?

YOU EXPECT ME TO **BELIEVE** YOU DIDN'T **KNOW** ABOUT THIS, INSPECTOR?

USE YOUR **GODDAMN HEAD.**

ANYTHING COMING OUT OF **THIS** OFFICE IN REGARD TO CORRIGAN IS **TAINTED** BECAUSE OF WHAT **WE** DID TO GET ALLEN OUT OF THE **JACKPOT** ON THE **LAMONICA** SHOOTING.

CORRIGAN **KNOWS** THAT.

AND **APPARENTLY** YOUR **PARTNER** DOES, **TOO.**

HE'S DOING THIS ON HIS **OWN?** ARE YOU TELLING ME THAT CRIS IS GOING AFTER CORRIGAN ON HIS **OWN?**

I'M NOT TELLING YOU **ANYTHING.**

BECAUSE IF I **DID** TELL YOU ANYTHING, IT WOULD MEAN I HAD **KNOWLEDGE** OF DETECTIVE ALLEN'S BUSINESS.

AND AS I **ALREADY** SAID, ANY **INVESTIGATION** OF JIM CORRIGAN'S **ILLEGAL** ACTIVITIES COMING FROM THIS **OFFICE** IS TAINTED.

JESUS CHRIST. HE'S TRYING TO **MAKE** IT **RIGHT.**

YOU **WEREN'T** HERE, DETECTIVE.

I **NEVER** SAW THAT **FOLDER** YOU'RE CARRYING, I DON'T EVEN **KNOW** IT **EXISTS...**

...AND IF YOU **WANT** YOUR PARTNER TO TAKE CORRIGAN **DOWN, NEITHER** DO **YOU,** UNDERSTAND?

M. ESPERANZA
INSPECTOR

YOU'RE AS **TAINTED** IN THIS AS I AM.

--TO HELL, LELAND! THIS IS THE **THIRD** TIME WE'VE BEEN CALLED **DOWN** HERE!

SHOW SOME **PITY**, OFFICER LONG. **ALL** THE **SHELTERS** ARE FULL-UP BECAUSE OF THE **SNOW**...

Sewood Furniture

FISH

TELL ME off FOR $2.00

...WE'RE JUST **LOOKING** TO STAY **WARM**.

DO IT SOMEPLACE ELSE. LIZ AND I HAVE TO COME DOWN HERE **AGAIN**, ALL OF **YOU** ARE GOING IN FOR **TRESPASSING**...

...AND **THIS** TIME THE **OWNER** SAYS HE'LL **PRESS** CHARGES.

'LEAST WE'D BE **WARM**.

WHARF bar

I AM SO SICK OF THE **STINK** OF PISS OFF THESE GUYS.

I **KNOW** THEY'RE **HOMELESS**, BUT FOR CHRIST'S SAKE, USE A DAMN **BATHROOM** ALREADY!

IS **THAT** KENZIE?

WHAT, THE **NARC**?

THINK **SO**. WAIT **HERE**.

STEVE!

JUST **WAIT**, DAMMIT!

130

KENZIE, YOU **SON OF A BITCH.**

...AND *THAT*, MY FRIENDS, BALANCES THE *BOOKS* NICELY.

ROURKE, YOU STILL LEANING ON ED KARL?

I *CAN* BE. YOU NEED SOMETHING PASSED ALONG?

YEAH, ABOUT *TEN* KEYS OF UNCUT *HEROIN.* TELL HIM I'LL BE IN *TOUCH* ABOUT THE *PRICE.*

JIMMY!

OFFICER LONG.

AND THE *LOVELY* OFFICER MULCAHEY.

HEY, BABY.

JIMMY, WE'VE GOT A *PROBLEM.*

THERE'S *NO* PROBLEM CAN'T BE *SOLVED,* STEVE, *RELAX.*

IT'S *KENZIE,* JIMMY.

HE'S *RATTING* YOU *OUT,* MAN...

...I SAW HIM *TALKING* TO THAT *M.C.U.* DETECTIVE, *ALLEN.*

WHEN WAS THIS?

NOT HALF AN HOUR AGO.

DAMMIT.

OKAY. OKAY...

...STEVE, I WANT YOU AND LIZ TO *DO* SOMETHING FOR ME...

RENEE! C'MON, YOU **KNOW** WHY I COULDN'T **TELL** YOU WHAT I WAS **DOING. SAME** REASON I CAN'T TELL ESPERANZA.

IS THAT WHAT THAT **CALL** WAS? THAT **WHY** YOU DIDN'T WANT ME **ALONG?**

I **CAN'T** TALK ABOUT THIS WITH **YOU!** YOU **CAN'T** BE ANYWHERE **NEAR** THIS INVESTIGATION.

I'M YOUR GODDAMN **PARTNER, CRIS!** I'M YOUR **BACKUP,** YOU DON'T **DO** THIS AND **NOT TELL** ME!

WHERE JIM CORRIGAN'S CONCERNED, **YEAH, I DO.**

I'M TAKING HIM **DOWN,** RENEE, AND I'M GONNA DO IT SO IT **STICKS.**

NO DISMISSALS, NO **DISAPPEARING** EVIDENCE, NO TECHNICALITIES, NO **DEALS...**

...I'M GOING TO **NAIL** THE BASTARD, AND IF **YOU'RE** INVOLVED, THEN YOU **JEOPARDIZE** THAT.

JUST TELL ME YOU'RE NOT DOING THIS **ALONE!**

TELL ME THAT YOU'VE GOT SAWYER **COVERING** YOUR **BACK,** SOMETHING LIKE THAT.

HOW THE HELL DO I DO **THAT?** THE **WHOLE** DAMN **DEPARTMENT** IS **CORRUPT,** RENEE!

I TELL **ANYBODY,** HOW LONG YOU THINK BEFORE ONE OF HIS **BUNKIES** FINDS OUT AND TIPS HIM TO ME, HUH?

YOU CAN **TRUST** THE CAPTAIN, YOU **KNOW** YOU CAN.

SOON AS I HAVE **ENOUGH** TO GET A **WARRANT,** I'LL BRING SAWYER **IN,** ALL RIGHT?

BUT **NOT** YET.

WHEN?

SOON.

ALL GOES WELL, **REAL** SOON.

HON? CAN YOU TAKE THE *BOYS* TO *SCHOOL* TOMORROW?

I'M SUPPOSED TO BE AT THE CLEARY STREET SITE FIRST THING IN THE MORNING TO GO OVER THE *BLUEPRINTS* WITH THE *FOREMAN*.

ALL RIGHT.

...SHE DID LAST NIGHT...

CHRIST, NOT *AGAIN*...

OH, CRIS...*TELL* ME YOU'RE NOT GOING OUT AGAIN.

POLICE

THIS SHOULD BE THE *LAST TIME*, DORE.

NO *FIGHTS* TONIGHT, HON?

NO PROMISES, JILL.

DON'T WAIT UP.

RIGHT, WHY SHOULD *BOTH* OF US LOSE OUT ON SLEEP?

CORRIGAN II PART TWO

...RESULTS OF THE CANVASS TO THE **CAPTAIN** WHEN SHE GETS BACK.

SHE'S WITH **MONTOYA?**

YEAH, PROBABLY BROKE IT TO HER FIRST SO SHE COULD COME **WITH** TO BREAK IT TO ALLEN'S **WIFE.**

CHRIST, HE HAD **KIDS,** DIDN'T HE? HE HAD --

YEAH, **TWO.** BOTH BOYS.

SARGE! SARGE!

YEAH, DAG?

I WANT YOU AND CROWE TO START PULLING ALLEN'S OLD CASES, CROSS-REF, SEE IF THERE'S ANYONE HE PUT INSIDE WHO'S **OUT.**

ON IT.

HE WAS WEARING HIS **VEST,** THAT'S THE THING, AND IT DIDN'T DO HIM A DAMN BIT OF **GOOD.**

WHAT PUNCHES THROUGH **KEVLAR** LIKE IT'S NOT EVEN **THERE?**

BULLOCK WAS AROUND, HE'D BE ABLE TO TELL YOU. NOT A THING THAT GUY DIDN'T KNOW ABOUT **GUNS.**

GONNA BE A COUPLE HOURS BEFORE WE GET A PRELIM ON THE **BALLISTICS,** THAT'S IF WE'RE **LUCKY...**

...I'D LIKE TO START NARROWING DOWN THE WEAPON **BEFORE** THEN.

VINCENT? YOU GOT ANYONE AT THE **F.B.I.** WHO COULD MAYBE HELP WITH THAT?

YEAH, MY **EX-WIFE.** I'LL GIVE HER A CALL --

CORRIGAN.

RENEE...

CORRIGAN DID IT.

CRIS WAS TRYING TO TAKE HIM *DOWN*...

...THERE'S A FILE...

...CRIS HAD A FILE HE'D PUT TOGETHER...

...IT'S NOT HERE...

RENEE, MAYBE YOU SHOULD...

...IT'S NOT *HERE*, IT WAS *RIGHT HERE*--

--WHERE THE F&%$ IS IT--

--WHERE THE F&%$ IS IT?!!

RENEE!

DAMMIT, DAMMIT, **DAMMIT,** IT WAS--

RENEE, YOU GOTTA RELAX--

--RIGHT HERE, HE **HAD** IT, IT WAS...

...RIGHT **HERE,** SEE?

YOU **SEE?**

YEAH, I SEE.

I'LL GIVE IT TO TOMMY AND DAG, THEY CAN START **WORKING** ON IT.

YOU AND ME, LET'S GO FOR A **WALK,** OKAY?

IT'S **CORRIGAN,** MARCUS. **CORRIGAN** DID IT...

...HE MURDERED **CRIS...**

...HE MURDERED MY **PARTNER.**

WHY DON'T YOU SIT DOWN?

NO...

...NO, I NEED TO GET *OUT* THERE, I NEED TO *HELP*...

JUST TAKE A COUPLE MINUTES, *OKAY*, RENEE?

CATCH YOUR *BREATH.*

I...I CAN'T *FEEL* ANYTHING, MARCUS...

...JUST...JUST THIS *ANGER*, THAT'S ALL THERE *IS*, AND...AND I DON'T KNOW WHAT TO *DO*, I DON'T KNOW WHAT I *SHOULD* DO...

...IT'S LIKE... IT'S LIKE...

...LIKE EVERYTHING'S WRAPPED IN *GRAY WOOL.*

LIKE YOU'RE *WATCHING* YOURSELF, BUT YOU'RE NOT IN *CONTROL.*

LIKE EVERYTHING YOU *FEEL*, EVERY-THING YOU *HEAR* IS COMING FROM FAR *AWAY.*

I KNOW. IT'S HOW I FELT AFTER *FREEZE* KILLED CHARLIE.

WHEN DOES IT *END?*

WHEN IT'S *OVER.*

LOUGHRIDGE!

HOW YOU *DOING*, CORRIGAN?

NOT TOO BAD, CLEM.

SO WHAT CAN I *DO* FOR YOU, JIMMY?

JUST MAKING SURE WE'VE GOT OUR *STORIES* STRAIGHT.

MMMM WE BETTER GO *OVER* IT AGAIN...

...THANKS FOR THE *LOAN*.

IT HAD QUITE A *KICK* TO IT.

YEAH, IT FIRES A BIG ROUND...

...MADE TO PUNCH THROUGH *BODY ARMOR*, OR SO I'M *TOLD*.

TECHNICALLY, IT'S A *RIFLE* ROUND, AND NOT A PISTOL ROUND AT *ALL*...

...AND SINCE WE BOTH KNOW YOU HAVE A *THING* FOR BIG *GUNS*...

EVER SINCE I WAS A LITTLE *GIRL* MMMM...

150

I JUST FINISHED THE *AUTOPSIES*, DETECTIVE BURKE. THERE'S *NO* NEED TO SPEAK THAT WAY TO MY STAFF.

THAT'S ONE OF *US* ON THE TABLE THERE, *DAMMIT*.

WHAT CAN YOU *TELL* US, NORA?

OFFICER LONG DIED FROM A MASSIVE HEMORRHAGE OF THE LEFT HEMITHORAX, BROUGHT ABOUT BY TWO *GUNSHOT WOUNDS* TO THE CHEST.

WE RECOVERED BOTH ROUNDS, AND HAVE SENT THEM TO *BALLISTICS*...

...PRESUMABLY THEY'LL MATCH WITH DETECTIVE ALLEN'S *DUTY WEAPON*.

WHAT ABOUT *CRIS?*

DETECTIVE ALLEN WAS SHOT FIVE TIMES IN THE BACK, EACH OF THE ROUNDS TRAVERSING THE THORAX AND PRESENTING CORRESPONDING *EXIT WOUNDS*.

ADDITIONALLY, I FOUND *KEVLAR* FRAGMENTS ALONG THE WOUND TRACKS THROUGHOUT THE THORAX.

GIVEN *THAT*, AND THE *SIZE* OF THE TRAUMA, I'D SAY YOU SHOULD BE LOOKING FOR A *RIFLE*.

WE RECOVERED ROUNDS AT THE SCENE, BALLISTICS IS TRYING TO *IDENTIFY* THEM.

DA-DA-DA-DAAA

DRIVER AND MACDONALD NOTED *POWDER STIPPLING* ALONG THE BACK OF CRIS' JACKET. THAT'S INDICATIVE OF A *PISTOL*.

BURKE.

I CAN'T SPEAK FOR WHAT MARCUS SAW, DETECTIVE PROCJNOW, BUT DETECTIVE ALLEN'S WOUNDS ARE CONSISTENT WITH ROUNDS FROM A RIFLE, *NOT* A PISTOL.

YEAH, GO *AHEAD*, VINCENT...

HOW'S DETECTIVE MONTOYA HOLDING UP?

ABOUT AS BADLY AS CAN BE EXPECTED...

OUTSTANDING! OKAY, RUN A CHECK--

...SHE HAD A PURE DISASSOCIATIVE MOMENT IN THE SQUAD ROOM ABOUT AN HOUR AGO, WASN'T PRETTY.

--YOU ALREADY DID?

NOTHING ABOUT THIS WORK IS PRETTY.

THEN BRING HIM IN, WE'LL BE RIGHT THERE!

DEL ARRAZIO THINKS HE'S I.D.ED THE WEAPON, SOME KIND OF MODIFIED GLOCK.

FIRES A ROUND CALLED THE .224 BOZ. IT PUNCHES THROUGH BODY ARMOR LIKE IT'S NOT EVEN THERE.

THAT FITS, THE .224 IS A RIFLE ROUND.

RIGHT, BUT THIS FIRES FROM A PISTOL.

THING IS, IT'S ONLY AVAILABLE TO LAW ENFORCEMENT, AND GUESS WHAT THE G.C.P.D. E.S.U. HAS SIX OF IN INVENTORY?

WHO'S THE RANGEMASTER FOR THE E.S.U.? LOUGHRIDGE?

DRIVER AND MACDONALD ARE BRINGING HIM IN FOR QUESTIONING RIGHT NOW.

LET'S ROAST THE BASTARD.

--WHY WE COULDN'T DO THIS DOWN AT THE RANGE.

YOU BRING ME IN *HERE*, YOU'RE MAKING ME FEEL LIKE I'VE DONE SOMETHING *WRONG*, GUYS.

HAVE YOU DONE SOMETHING WRONG, SERGEANT LOUGHRIDGE?

DON'T PLAY ME LIKE THAT, DRIVER. I'M ON THE *JOB*, JUST LIKE *YOU* GUYS.

YOU GOT A *QUESTION* FOR ME, JUST *ASK* IT.

HOW MANY *G-TWO-TWO-FOUR SEMI-AUTOS* YOU GOT IN E.S.U. INVENTORY, SARGE?

SIX, ALL OF THEM *ACCOUNTED* FOR.

YOU SIGN ANY OF THEM *OUT* IN THE LAST DAY OR SO?

NO.

GNNNT! *WRONG* ANSWER!

AND BEFORE YOU *THINK* OF STICKING TO YOUR LAME-ASS *LIES*, SARGE...

...ALLOW ME TO INFORM YOU THAT WE THINK ONE OF YOUR TWO-TWO-FOURS WAS USED IN A *CAPITAL CRIME*.

WHICH MAKES YOU AN *ACCESSORY*, AND FIRST IN LINE FOR THE *ELECTRIC CHAIR*.

CARE TO TRY *AGAIN*?

CALM *DOWN*, MAN!

I SAID I DIDN'T *SIGN* ANY OF THEM *OUT*...

...BUT *MAYBE* I LET SOMEONE *BORROW* ONE AS A *FAVOR*...

YOU RAN AT HIM WITHOUT *US?*

COOL YOUR *JETS,* DAG, WE *GOT* WHAT YOU NEED.

SERGEANT LOUGHRIDGE COPS TO THE FACT THAT HE *RENTS OUT* SOME OF THE ARSENAL ON THE *SIDE.*

SEEMS THAT CORRIGAN QUOTE RENTED UNQUOTE ONE OF THE TWO-TWO-FOURS YESTERDAY AFTERNOON TO GO *SHOOTING* WITH HIS GIRLFRIEND, RETURNED IT THIS *MORNING.*

SON OF A *BITCH.* HE SAY WHICH *ONE?*

YEAH, BUT I'M THINKING WE SHOULD RUN THEM *ALL* TO BALLISTICS, JUST TO BE ON THE SAFE SIDE.

GETS BETTER. THE GIRLFRIEND, *MULCAHEY?* SHE WAS OFFICER LONG'S *PARTNER...*

RENEE. WE'RE GOING TO *GET* HIM, DON'T WORRY.

WE'LL *FIND* THE WEAPON. WE'RE GOING TO *NAIL* CORRIGAN.

--GET WARRANTS FROM THE D.A. FOR THE GUNS *RIGHT NOW*.

IN THE *MEANTIME*, I WANT BOTH *CORRIGAN* AND *MULCAHEY* IN FOR QUESTIONING.

HE'LL HAVE *COACHED* HER ON THE *ALIBI*, CAPTAIN --

IT'S A *SET-UP*.

HOW DO YOU FIGURE?

LOUGHRIDGE GAVE CORRIGAN UP BECAUSE THAT'S WHAT CORRIGAN *WANTED* HIM TO DO.

YOU THINK MAYBE YOU'RE A LITTLE *BLIND* ON THIS ONE, RENEE?

WE'LL *FIND* THE GUN, RENEE, GOD AS MY *WITNESS*.

LOUGHRIDGE ALREADY PUT IT IN CORRIGAN'S *HANDS*, ALL WE HAVE TO DO IS PROVE IT'S THE *SAME* WEAPON THAT KILLED *CRIS*...

...AS SOON AS WE FIND THE GUN, *CLEM* DOWN IN *BALLISTICS* CAN *MATCH* IT WITH THE ROUNDS RECOVERED AT THE *SCENE*.

WE'RE GOING TO *GET* HIM, *TRUST* ME.

FIND THAT GUN.

AND BRING *CORRIGAN* AND *MULCAHEY* IN FOR QUESTIONING.

YOU GUYS GRAB MULCAHEY, **WE'LL** PICK UP **CORRIGAN.**

DO ME A FAVOR, DAGMAR, LET **US** COLLECT THE GUNS, OKAY?

I'VE GOT A GOOD **FEELING** ABOUT THIS.

FINE.

VINCENT!

DAG?

NEED YOU AND JOELY TO PICK UP LONG'S PARTNER, **REBECCA MULCAHEY.**

BRING HER IN FOR QUESTIONING.

OUR **PLEASURE.**

UH...IS THERE A **PROBLEM**, DETECTIVE DRIVER?

EXERCISING A **WARRANT**, STEFANO. WHERE ARE THE G-TWO-TWO-FOURS--

OVER HERE.

ALL **RIGHT**, I'M **COMING**, DAMMIT --

BZZZT BZZZT

JIMMY.

YEAH, I **KNOW**.

COME TO **MOMMA**.

--STOP LEANING ON THE **BUZZER**...

OFFICER MULCAHEY?

I'M **DETECTIVE BARTLETT**, THIS IS **SERGEANT DEL ARRAZIO**. WE WERE HOPING YOU'D **ACCOMPANY** US BACK TO **CENTRAL**...

...TO HELP US ANSWER A FEW **QUESTIONS**. YOU DON'T MIND COMING WITH US, **DO YOU, JIMMY?**

IT'D BE MY **PLEASURE**, DETECTIVE **BURKE**...

...ANYTHING TO **HELP**...

DETECTIVE? DETECTIVE... I, UH...

...I BROUGHT YOU A CUP OF COFFEE.

BLACK, HOW YOU LIKE IT.

THANKS, STACY.

I'LL UH... I'LL BE AT MY DESK...

RENEE?

DORE.

THIS IS THE WORST DAMN DAY OF MY LIFE, RENEE.

TELL ME ABOUT IT.

AH, DAMMIT... ...THOUGHT I WAS FINISHED CRYING FOR NOW.

NO, IT'S OKAY.

C'MON, WE'LL TALK IN THE BREAK ROOM.

DARIA SAID YOU'VE BEEN HERE ALL DAY.

THAT YOU CAME STRAIGHT HERE WHEN YOU GOT...WHEN YOU GOT THE *NEWS.*

YEAH.

THE BOYS AND I WERE HOPING TO SEE YOU.

I *KNOW,* I'M SORRY.

HOW...HOW ARE *JAKE* AND *MAL* DOING?

IT HASN'T REALLY *SUNK IN* YET.

I WAS GOING TO TAKE THEM TO MY *SISTER'S* IN *DETROIT,* BUT *DARIA* OFFERED TO STAY WITH THEM.

I'LL COME OVER *TONIGHT,* IF YOU WANT.

WE'D *LIKE* THAT.

WHY DIDN'T YOU COME WITH CAPTAIN SAWYER TO BREAK THE *NEWS,* RENEE?

WE...WE REALLY *NEEDED* YOU.

I WANTED TO. I *COULDN'T.*

I'M SO *ANGRY,* DORE...AND I DIDN'T WANT TO BRING THAT INTO YOUR *GRIEF.*

IT'S *YOUR* GRIEF, TOO.

IT'S NOT THE SAME.

THEY'RE BRINGING THE GUY *IN*, DORE.

YOU'VE GOT A *SUSPECT?*

HE'S NOT A SUSPECT. HE *DID* IT.

AND I'M *TERRIFIED* HE'S GOING TO *WALK.*

CRIS *LOVED* BEING A COP.

EVEN *HERE,* IN *GOTHAM,* WITH ALL OF THE *CORRUPTION,* WITH ALL OF THE *EVIL,* HE LOVED IT.

BECAUSE EVEN HERE, IN GOTHAM, HE *BELIEVED* IN IT.

HE BELIEVED IN WHAT *YOU* DID, IN WHAT *HE* DID...

"...AND I DO, TOO, RENEE...

"...RIGHT NOW, I HAVE TO...

"...WHAT CHOICE DO I HAVE? BECAUSE IF I DON'T...

"...OH, LORD, IF I DON'T, RENEE...

"...THEN MY HUSBAND HAS DIED FOR NOTHING..."

CORRIGAN II

PART
THREE

SORRY TO HEAR ABOUT YOUR PARTNER.

YEAH. YEAH, IT PRETTY MUCH *SUCKS.*

YOU AND LONG HAD BEEN *PARTNERED* FOR, WHAT, THREE YEARS?

WHY'D YOU BRING IN BECKY?

OFFICER MULCAHEY WAS *PARTNERED* WITH OFFICER LONG.

WE'RE HOPING SHE MIGHT *KNOW* WHY LONG TRIED TO KILL DETECTIVE ALLEN.

HEY, HE WAS MY *PARTNER,* NOT MY *LOVER.*

JUST BECAUSE WE *RODE* TOGETHER DOESN'T MEAN I KNOW WHAT HE WAS *INTO.*

DID HE *KNOW* DETECTIVE KENZIE IN NARCOTICS?

YOU THINK LONG KILLED KENZIE, THEN TRIED TO KILL ALLEN?

DON'T YOU?

C'MON, DETECTIVE PROCJNOW, MY JOB IS TO *COLLECT* THE EVIDENCE, *NOT* TO INTERPRET IT.

NO, I WAS OUT WITH *JIMMY,* AS I'M SURE YOU ALREADY *KNOW,* DETECTIVE DEL ARRAZIO.

DOING WHAT?

WE WENT *SHOOTING.*

NO, NOT AT THE RANGE, WE WENT OUT TO BRENTWOOD.

TO THE WOODS.

DID ANYONE *SEE* YOU?

WE WENT OUT TO THE WOODS SO WE WOULDN'T *DISTURB* ANYONE, DETECTIVE, OF COURSE NOBODY SAW US.

WHY NOT GO SHOOTING ON THE *RANGE*? YOU'VE GOT *ACCESS*.

WE WANTED *PRIVACY*, DETECTIVE. NOTHING WRONG WITH THAT, IS THERE?

YOU SURE YOU WANT TO WATCH THIS, RENEE?

I'M SURE, CAPTAIN.

THING IS, JIMMY, THAT MAKES OFFICER MULCAHEY YOUR *ALIBI*.

ALIBI? FOR *WHAT*?

HOW MUCH DID YOU PAY BILL KENZIE TO *UNDERCOUNT* THE DOPE HIS NARCOTICS SQUAD *CONFISCATED*?

WHAT?

HE TOLD DETECTIVE ALLEN YOU'D PAID HIM OVER *SIXTY GRAND* IN THE LAST THREE YEARS.

SIXTY GRAND... THAT'S...THAT'S A *LOT* OF *MONEY*, JIMMY.

WHICH MEANS YOU WERE PULLING IN A LOT *MORE* THAN *THAT*...

GO GET HIM, DAGMAR.

I DON'T KNOW ANYTHING ABOUT THAT.

I ALREADY TOLD YOU, JIMMY AND I WENT SHOOTING.

ALL RIGHT, LET'S TALK ABOUT THAT, THEN.

WHAT'S UP WITH THAT? WHY WEREN'T YOU AT THE RANGE?

WE WANTED PRIVACY.

WHAT CAN I TELL YOU, SARGE? GUNS GET ME HOT.

YOU AND ME BOTH.

JUST GOT A TITANIUM SLIDE P99 FOR MY COLLECTION, YOU WOULDN'T BELIEVE HOW SWEET THIS PISTOL IS.

YOU GET THAT IN NINE?

S&W FORTY, WITH THE LAW-ENFORCEMENT MAGAZINES.

OH, DAMN, THAT'S SWEET.

YOU GOTTA GO WITH THE FORTY, I JUST GOT AN HK P2000 IN FORTY.

WHAT ABOUT TWO-TWO-FOUR?

THAT'S A RIFLE ROUND, SARGE, NOT A PISTOL ROUND.

C'MON, OFFICER. DON'T TELL ME YOU'RE A PISTOL ENTHUSIAST AND THEN PRETEND NOT TO KNOW ABOUT THE BOZ TWO-TWO-FOUR.

YOU NEED A MODIFIED GLOCK TO FIRE THE BOZ ROUND, IT'S CALLED A G-224, AND ONLY E.S.U. HAS ACCESS TO THOSE, SMART-ASS.

THEN WHAT WAS CORRIGAN DOING WITH ONE LAST NIGHT?

--HIM TWO HUNDRED BUCKS TO **LOAN** ME ONE, THAT'S ALL! THERE ARE SIX OF THEM, JUST SITTING IN INVENTORY!

I BROUGHT IT BACK THIS MORNING, NO HARM, NO FOUL!

SO YOU'RE ADMITTING YOU TOOK ONE OF THE G-224's FROM E.S.U. INVENTORY?

YOU TOOK A GUN MADE TO BLOW THROUGH BODY ARMOR FROM E.S.U. INVENTORY YESTERDAY, THAT'S WHAT YOU'RE SAYING?

BECKY WANTED TO TAKE ONE SHOOTING, THAT'S--

INTERESTING. WE'VE GOT **THREE** BODIES...

...KENZIE, WHO WASN'T WEARING BODY ARMOR...

...AND BESIDES, THE BULLET THROUGH HIS HEAD CAME FROM THE GUN WE FOUND ON OFFICER LONG...

...AND NO VEST ON OFFICER LONG HIMSELF, OR ELSE ALLEN'S SHOTS WOULDN'T HAVE **KILLED** HIM...

CAPTAIN?

...BUT HERE'S DETECTIVE ALLEN, **WEARING** HIS KEVLAR...

WE'VE GOT A PROBLEM WITH THE BALLISTICS REPORT.

...AND YOU JUST PUT THE GUN THAT **KILLED** HIM IN **YOUR** HAND.

PROVE IT.

WHAT THE HELL'S HAPPENED?

ROBINS &&#*ED US, THAT'S WHAT &*%&ING HAPPENED!

EXPLAIN.

WE BROUGHT ALL SIX OF THE G-224s IN FOR TESTING, INCLUDING THE MURDER WEAPON, SWEAR TO GOD.

ROBINS SAYS NONE OF THE GUNS MATCH, HE SAYS THE ROUNDS THAT KILLED CRIS CAME FROM A &*%#ING RIFLE...

...A BUSHMASTER .223, LIKE THE BELTWAY SNIPERS USED, AND NOT FROM A G-224.

SON OF A BITCH.

HE THINKS MAYBE THE ROUNDS ARE HANDLOADS, CUSTOM MADE, TO GO WITH THE RIFLE THAT SHOT CRIS.

HE'S LYING! I HAD THE DAMN PISTOL IN MY HAND, CAPTAIN!

YOU HAD IT? WHAT DO YOU MEAN, YOU HAD IT?

I JUST...I KNOW HE'S LYING, CAPTAIN.

CORRIGAN BOUGHT HIM OFF, SOMETHING, HE'S LYING.

SO WE CAN PUT THE GUN IN CORRIGAN'S HAND, BUT WE CAN'T PROVE IT'S THE WEAPON THAT KILLED CRIS.

SON OF A BITCH...

...HE PLAYED US...

--GETTING TOO **CLOSE?** WAS ALLEN FINALLY GOING TO TAKE YOU **DOWN,** YOU CORRUPT LITTLE MOTHER&&*(#+!?

PEOPLE HAVE BEEN ACCUSING ME OF THINGS FOR **YEARS,** DETECTIVE BURKE.

LIKE I SAID BEFORE...

...PROVE IT.

DETECTIVES.

A MOMENT, PLEASE.

GET OUT OF HERE.

I'M SORRY?

YOU HEARD ME.

YOU KNOW WHERE TO FIND ME IF YOU WANT TO TRY AGAIN.

THIS ISN'T OVER.

DON'T JUST STAND AROUND LICKING YOUR WOUNDS, GET OUT THERE AND *MAKE THE DAMN CASE.*

MACDONALD'S SO SURE WE HAVE THE *MURDER WEAPON,* TAKE IT TO THE BUREAU FOR *FURTHER* TESTING.

IF CORRIGAN BOUGHT ROBINS AND LOUGHRIDGE *OFF,* FIND THE *MONEY.*

THIS ISN'T OVER.

SURE IT IS.

WHAT WAS THAT?

C'MON, THE *WHOLE CASE* RESTED ON THE *WEAPON* AND THE BUREAU WON'T BE ABLE TO MAKE THE *MATCH.*

THERE'S NO WAY ROBINS DIDN'T DO A *BARREL SWAP* ON THE GUN, *SOMETHING* TO &%*& THAT UP.

SO WE JUST GIVE *UP,* THAT'S IT? LET THAT COP-KILLING *&#%SUCKER *WALK?*

C'MON, SARGE, *YOU* KNOW THAT'S NOT WHAT I MEANT.

HEY.

THEN YOU TELL ME WHAT YOU *DID* MEAN, MARCUS, BECAUSE IT SOUNDS LIKE YOU DON'T *CARE* IF CRIS' NAME STAYS IN THE *RED!*

HEY, IT'S NOT *MY* FAULT YOU COULDN'T GET MULCAHEY TO ROLL OVER ON HER *BOYFRIEND--*

HEY!

ANYBODY SEEN *RENEE?*

BEG YOUR PARDON.

...FOR THE FUNERAL, THAT'LL BE THURSDAY...

...HIS BROTHER IN DETROIT GETS IN LATER TONIGHT, GRACE AND I'LL PICK HIM UP...

...COFFEE? FEET AND LIGHT, RIGHT?

...MAKE AN ARREST...

...AT ST. AGNES', I THINK, BUT I'M NOT SURE...

YOU TRY THE BUTTER COOKIES? THESE ARE OUTSTANDING.

UNCLE GARY? YOU AND AUNT GRACE STAYING TONIGHT?

YEAH, WE'RE STAYING, MAL. LONG AS YOU AND YOUR MOM NEED US.

YEAH, I CAN HEAR YOUR ARTERIES HARDENING FROM HERE.

MRS. ALLEN? I THOUGHT YOU MIGHT LIKE A PLATE.

IT'S VIOLET, DEAR. THANK YOU.

HEY, RENEE! WHAT'S THE GOOD WORD?

CORRIGAN WALKED.

173

MAKE SURE JAKE AND MAL *EAT* SOMETHING, *WOULD* YOU, THERESE?

SURE, MRS. ALLEN.

RENEE! I DIDN'T SEE YOU COME *IN.*

JUST *GOT* HERE.

ARE YOU *HUNGRY?*

DARIA'S BEEN COOKING *COMFORT FOOD* ALL *DAY,* WE'VE GOT LAMB STEW AND MAC AND CHEESE, JUST ABOUT ANYTHING YOU COULD *WANT.*

I'M FINE, THANKS, DORE.

HOW DID IT GO WITH THE *SUSPECTS* THEY BROUGHT IN? WITH *CORRIGAN* AND THAT *WOMAN?*

WE'RE MAKING PROGRESS.

THESE THINGS TAKE *TIME.*

I JUST WANTED TO CHECK IN WITH YOU, THAT'S ALL.

I'M GONNA *GO,* THERE'S SOME STUFF I NEED TO *DO.*

YOU'RE SURE YOU WON'T *STAY* FOR A BIT?

I CAN'T. I'M *SORRY.*

WHAT ARE YOU *DOING* OUT HERE, JAKE?

NOTHING.

YOUR MOM *KNOW* YOU'RE SMOKING?

NO.

MY DAD'S NEVER COMING *HOME*, RENEE.

HE'S *NEVER* COMING HOME.

I KNOW.

I KEEP ASKING MYSELF THE SAME THING, RENEE.

AND I *HATE* MYSELF FOR ASKING IT, BUT I KEEP ASKING IT *ANYWAY*, I CAN'T HELP IT.

WHY WASN'T IT *YOU?*

I KEEP ASKING *MYSELF* THAT ONE, TOO.

YOU WANT ME TO CALL YOU A CAB, HON?

S'ALLRIGHT.

KEEP THE CHANGE.

CORRIGAN.

CORRIGAN!

YOU MOTHER-#$%¢!

...GONNA HAVE THE FUNERAL?

TOMORROW AFTERNOON.

COMMISSIONER AKINS SAYS IT'S FULL-DRESS...

RENEE...

DETECTIVE, WHAT'RE *YOU* DOING HERE?

YOU SHOULD BE AT *HOME*...

...YOU NEED SOME *TIME*--

MORE THAN YOU KNOW.

I CAN'T *DO* IT ANYMORE, CAPTAIN.

GOTHAM CENTRAL #33 • ART BY SEAN PHILLIPS

GOTHAM CENTRAL #35 • ART BY SEAN PHILLIPS

GOTHAM CENTRAL #36 • ART BY JOSH MIDDLETON

GOTHAM CENTRAL #37 • ART BY SEAN PHILLIPS

GOTHAM CENTRAL #39 · ART BY SEAN PHILLIPS

GOTHAM CENTRAL #40 • ART BY SEAN PHILLIPS